Workbook

DIMENSIONS MATH 7A

a Singapore Math® Program

 STAR PUBLISHING PTE LTD

 SM Singapore Math Inc®

STAR PUBLISHING PTE LTD

115A Commonwealth Drive #05-12
Singapore 149596
Tel: (65) 64796800
Website: www.starpub.com.sg
Email: contactus@starpub.com.sg

in association with

Singapore Math Inc*

Singapore Math Inc
19535 SW 129th Avenue
Tualatin, OR 97062
Website: www.SingaporeMath.com
Email: customerservice@singaporemath.com

First published 2013
Reprinted 2014
Reprinted 2015
Reprinted 2017
Reprinted 2018
Dimensions Math has been adapted from *Discovering Mathematics*, first published by Star Publishing Pte Ltd in 2007.

ISBN 978-981-4431-74-3

Printed by KHL Printing Co Pte Ltd, Singapore

PREFACE

The **Dimensions Math Workbooks** are designed for middle school students. Developed in collaboration between Star Publishing Pte. Ltd. and Singapore Math Inc., these workbooks follow the Singapore Mathematics Framework and also cover the topics in the Common Core State Standards.

Each workbook is written as a supplement to the textbook, *Dimensions Math*, to give students more practice in applying the concepts learned. Students may refer to the summary of the important concepts in each chapter of the textbook for a quick review before attempting the questions in the workbook. After completing the exercises, students will not only polish their own analytical skills, but also develop a stronger foundation in mathematics.

The questions in each workbook chapter are categorized into 4 parts according to the level of difficulty and the thinking skills involved:

- *Basic Practice*: simple questions that drill comprehension of concepts
- *Further Practice*: harder questions that involve direct applications
- *Challenging Practice*: questions that require synthesis ability
- *Enrichment*: questions that demand higher order thinking

These questions encourage students to think analytically, reason logically, use appropriate connections between mathematical ideas, and apply problem-solving skills in daily life situations.

We hope that these comprehensive workbooks will give students the tools and the confidence to handle mathematical questions and apply mathematical concepts to real-life situations. By achieving this, students will find learning mathematic an interesting and exciting experience.

We also wish to express our sincere thanks to Mr Chow Wai Keung and Mr Yong Fook Meng (the Co-authors) for the work and efforts in the original series, *Discovering Mathematics*.

CONTENTS

1 Factors And Multiples

Basic Practice

1. List all the factors of each of the following numbers.

    (a) 18   **(b)** 20

    (c) 24   **(d)** 30

    (e) 45   **(f)** 50

    (g) 63

2. Write down the first five multiples of each of the following numbers.

    (a) 4   **(b)** 15

    (c) 17   **(d)** 21

    (e) 35   **(f)** 42

    (g) 100

3. Simplify and express the following in exponential notation.

    (a) $2 \times 2 \times 2 \times 2 \times 2$

    (b) $2 \times 2 \times 3 \times 3 \times 3 \times 3$

    (c) $7 \times 4 \times 7 \times 4 \times 7 \times 4 \times 7$

    (d) $5 \times 8 \times 8 \times 8 \times 5 \times 5 \times 5$

    (e) $\dfrac{11 \times 11 \times 11 \times 11 \times 11}{11 \times 11}$

    (f) $\dfrac{3 \times 3 \times 3 \times 7 \times 7 \times 7 \times 7}{3 \times 7}$

4. Find the prime factorization of the following numbers and express your answers in exponential notation.

    (a) 96   **(b)** 120

    (c) 144   **(d)** 600

    (e) 675   **(f)** 1,000

    (g) 1,323

5. Find the prime factorization of the following and express your answers in exponential notation.

    (a) 4×4 **(b)** $6 \times 6 \times 6$

    (c) $3 \times 3 \times 3 \times 6 \times 6$ **(d)** $10 \times 10 \times 2 \times 5 \times 5$

    (e) $12 \times 14 \times 21$

6. Find the GCF of each pair of numbers.

(a) 9 and 36

(b) 12 and 30

(c) 24 and 64

(d) 6 and 35

(e) 63 and 147

(f) 98 and 112

(g) 117 and 195

(h) 108 and 198

(i) 245 and 392

7. Find the LCM of each pair of numbers.

(a) 4 and 10

(b) 6 and 9

(c) 8 and 15

(d) 14 and 16

(e) 15 and 18

(f) 24 and 36

(g) 34 and 51

(h) 36 and 63

(i) 105 and 150

8. Find the positive square root of each of the following numbers.

(a) 64

(b) 144

(c) 256

(d) 324

(e) 400

(f) 576

(g) 625

9. Find the cube root of each of the following numbers.

(a) 27

(b) 64

(c) 125

(d) 1,000

(e) 1,728

(f) 2,744

(g) 4,096

10. Determine whether each of the following sentences is true or false. For each false sentence, give an example to show it is false.

(a) All odd numbers greater than 1 but less than 10 are prime numbers.

(b) An even number cannot be a prime number.

(c) A prime number cannot be a perfect square.

(d) A prime number cannot be a perfect cube.

Further Practice

11. Express each of the following as a single number in exponential notation.

(a) $5^3 \times 5^4$

(b) $7^4 \times 7^2$

(c) $2^6 \div 2^3$

(d) $(3^4)^2$

(e) $(3^2 \times 3^5)^2$

(f) $(5^8 \div 5^4)^2$

(g) $(7^4)^2 \times (7^2)^3$

12. Find the GCF of each group of numbers.
    (a) 30, 42, and 84
    (b) 35, 42, and 56
    (c) 45, 78, and 96
    (d) 51, 85, and 102
    (e) 69, 115, and 138
    (f) 75, 105, and 135
    (g) 81, 108, and 180
    (h) 105, 147, and 231

13. Find the LCM of each group of numbers.
    (a) 5, 18, and 20
    (b) 12, 14, and 18
    (c) 3, 34, and 46
    (d) 16, 24, and 56
    (e) 22, 55, and 77
    (f) 24, 35, and 49
    (g) 8, 44, and 105
    (h) 225, 245, and 280

14. (a) Find the prime factorization of 3,375 and write your answer in exponential notation.
    (b) Hence, deduce and write down
         (i)   the smallest 2-digit number that is a factor of 3,375,
         (ii)   the largest 2-digit number that is a factor of 3,375,
         (iii) the smallest 3-digit number that is a factor of 3,375,
         (iv)   the smallest 4-digit number that is a factor of 3,375.

15. (a) Find the prime factorization of the following numbers and write your answers in exponential notation.
         (i)   27
         (ii)   99
         (iii) 135
    (b) Hence, find
         (i)   the GCF of 27, 99, and 135 in prime factorization form,
         (ii)   the LCM of 27, 99, and 135 in prime factorization form.

16. (a) Find the prime factorization of the following numbers and write your answers in exponential notation.
         (i)   324
         (ii)   432
    (b) Hence, find the smallest possible value of
         (i)   a whole number w if $432 \times w$ is a multiple of 324,
         (ii)   a whole number x if $324 \times x$ is a multiple of 432.

17. (a) Find the smallest possible value of
         (i)   a whole number y if it leaves a remainder of 3 when divided by 5, 6, or 9,
         (ii)   a whole number z if it leaves a remainder of 2 when divided by 4, 5, or 6.
    (b) Hence, calculate the
         (i)   GCF of y and z,
         (ii)   LCM of y and z.

18. (a) Find the prime factorization of 648 and write your answer in exponential notation.
    (b) Hence, find
        (i)   the smallest possible value of a whole number m if $648 \times m$ is a perfect square,
        (ii) the smallest possible value of a whole number n if $648 \times n$ is a perfect cube.

19. (a) Find the prime factorization of 12,600 and write your answer in exponential notation.
    (b) Hence, evaluate each of the following and express your answer in prime factorization form.

        (i) $\sqrt{14 \times 12{,}600}$ (ii) $\sqrt{\dfrac{7 \times 12{,}600}{2}}$

        (iii) $\sqrt[3]{\dfrac{15 \times 12{,}600}{7}}$

20. (a) Simplify and express $\dfrac{2^8 \times 5^7}{20}$ in prime factorization form.
    (b) Hence, find in prime factorization form,

        (i)   the positive square root of $\dfrac{2^8 \times 5^7}{20}$,

        (ii) the cube root of $\dfrac{2^8 \times 5^7}{20}$.

Challenging Practice

21. The length, width, and height of an open rectangular container are 90 cm, 45 cm, and 30 cm respectively.
    (a) Suppose identical cubes are placed within the container such that they fill up the container completely. Calculate
        (i)   in cm, the greatest possible length of each cube,
        (ii) in cm^3, the corresponding volume of each cube.
    (b) How many cubes described in (a) are placed inside the container?

22. A company planned to donate 640 packs of cookies, 320 bottles of mineral water, and $800 worth of cash to a senior center. Suppose that the maximum number of packs of cookies, bottles of mineral water, and cash are to be placed equally in gift bags before the donation.
    (a) How many gift bags are needed?
    (b) List the content in each gift bag.

23. Students in a middle school are invited by the organizer of a parade to form a marching contingent. The organizer states that all the rows should have the same number of students. However, it has not been decided if the participants of the contingent are to march in 4s, 5s, or 6s. If 200 students are available for training, calculate
    (a) the maximum possible size of the marching contingent if participants were to be trained to march in 4s, 5s, or 6s,
    (b) the number of participants who will be put on reserve.

24. (a) Find the LCM of 5, 6, and 8.

(b) Suppose trains on each of three separate lines (North-South, East-West, and North-East) leave together at 2.30 P.M., which falls within the non-peak period from 2 P.M. to 5 P.M. Suppose also that the trains on the North-South, East-West, and North-East lines leave regularly at 5-minute, 6-minute, and 8-minute intervals respectively during the non-peak period.

(i) How long, in hours, will it take for the trains on all the three lines to leave together again?

(ii) Write down the time that corresponds to your answer in **(i)**.

25. (a) A cubical cake of volume 2,744 cm³ rests on a flat surface. Calculate

(i) the length of a side of the cake,

(ii) the perimeter of the face of the cake which rests on the flat surface,

(iii) the area of the face of the cake which rests on the flat surface.

(b) Three cuts are made on the cake. The first two cuts are made from the top of the cake as shown by the dotted lines in the diagram below (on the left). The third cut is made horizontally from the side of the cake as shown by the dotted line in the diagram below (on the right).

(i) How many portions is the cake cut into?

(ii) Are all the portions cubical if each portion is of equal volume? Explain your answer.

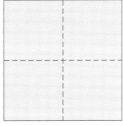

top view of cake

side view of cake

Enrichment

26. Between the years 2000 and 2100, leap years occur every 4 years. The leap day, February 29, occurred on a Friday in 2008.

(a) Write down 3 leap years between the years 2000 and 2100 apart from 2008 and 2016.

(b) Describe a common property of the numbers of the leap years.

(c) What day of the week is February 29, 2016?

27. Mrs. Moss has 3 school-going children. The product of the ages of herself and her 3 children is 20,295.

(a) Find the age of Mrs. Moss.

(b) Find the possible ages of the 3 children.

(c) If the sum of the ages of the 3 children is 25, find the age of the youngest child.

28. (a) List all the prime numbers less than 20.

(b) Find the number of ways to select two of the numbers in **(a)**.

(c) Find the number of ways in **(b)** such that the sum of the selected numbers is a prime.

29. There are about 400 to 500 pieces of rectangular tiles in a construction site. The dimensions of each tile are 63 cm by 28 cm.

    (a) If the tiles are used to lay a square, what is the least number of tiles required? What is the length of a side of the square then?

    (b) If a tile is divided into identical small squares, what is the maximum length of a side of a small square?

    (c) The tiles can be divided into 5, 6, or 8 square groups. Find the total number of tiles.

2 Real Numbers

Basic Practice

1. Fill in the blanks with '<' or '>'.
   (a) 3 _____ 7
   (b) 18 _____ 14
   (c) −5 _____ 3
   (d) −6 _____ 8
   (e) 7 _____ −2
   (f) 1 _____ −12
   (g) −2 _____ −6
   (h) −24 _____ −15

2. State the numbers represented by the points A, B, C, D, E, F, G, and H on the number line.

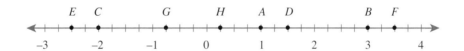

3. (a) Represent each pair of numbers on a number line and write down their relation using the '<' sign.
   (i) 3, −2
   (ii) −3, 1.5
   (iii) $-\dfrac{1}{2}, -4$
   (b) Represent each pair of numbers on a number line and write down their relation using the '>' sign.
   (i) $-2, 4\dfrac{1}{2}$
   (ii) 1, −0.5
   (iii) $-3\dfrac{1}{2}, -1.5$

(Solve)
4. Evaluate the following.
   (a) 12 + (−5) =
   (b) 18 + (−18) =
   (c) (−6) + 14 =
   (d) (−8) − 9 =
   (e) 33 − (−33) =
   (f) (−36) + (−14) =
   (g) −(−24) + (−13) =
   (h) −(−35) − (−15) =

5. (a) Simplify each of the following values.
   (i) $|5|$
   (ii) $|36|$
   (iii) $|-21|$
   (iv) $|-18|$
   (b) Hence, find the sum of all the values in (a).

6. Evaluate the following.
(a) $(-6) \times 7$
(b) $15 \times (-4)$
(c) $(-5) \times (-8)$
(d) $24 \div (-3)$
(e) $(-48) \div 12$
(f) $(-72) \div (-18)$
(g) $(-5)^2$
(h) $(-5)^3$
(i) -3^2
(j) -3^3

7. Express each of the following rational numbers in its simplest form.
(a) $\dfrac{15}{35}$
(b) $\dfrac{16}{40}$
(c) $\dfrac{84}{24}$
(d) $-\dfrac{54}{72}$
(e) $-\dfrac{57}{18}$
(f) $-\dfrac{100}{64}$

8. Evaluate the following, giving your answers in the simplest form.
(a) $\dfrac{5}{8} + \dfrac{1}{2}$
(b) $3\dfrac{1}{12} - 1\dfrac{7}{8}$
(c) $\dfrac{7}{15} \times \dfrac{5}{21}$
(d) $\left(-1\dfrac{4}{5}\right) \times \dfrac{45}{3}$
(e) $\left(-\dfrac{81}{8}\right) \times \left(-\dfrac{16}{27}\right)$
(f) $\left(-\dfrac{27}{40}\right) \div \dfrac{9}{8}$
(g) $-\left(\dfrac{2}{5}\right)^2 \div \dfrac{21}{100}$
(h) $\dfrac{7}{4} + \left(-\dfrac{35}{16}\right) \times \dfrac{2}{7}$

9. Express the following as decimals.
(a) $\dfrac{3}{8}$
(b) $2\dfrac{13}{20}$
(c) $-\dfrac{3}{40}$
(d) $-1\dfrac{7}{8}$
(e) $-3\dfrac{3}{50}$
(f) $\left(\dfrac{3}{5}\right)^2$
(g) $\left(-1\dfrac{7}{10}\right)^2$
(h) $\left(-\dfrac{1}{2}\right)^3$

10. (a) Arrange 0.72, 0.088, -1, $-\dfrac{2}{3}$, and $\dfrac{9}{2}$ in ascending order.

(b) Arrange -2.5, -5, $\dfrac{1}{5}$, $-\dfrac{3}{2}$, and 0.69 in descending order.

11. Evaluate the following using a calculator.
(a) $5^2 + \dfrac{3}{8}$
(b) $4^3 - 52\dfrac{7}{20}$
(c) $\sqrt{76}$
(d) $\sqrt[3]{100}$
(e) $\sqrt[3]{445} - \sqrt{93}$
(f) $-6 \times (-8 + 19)$
(g) $-54 \div [(-16) \times (-27)]$
(h) $[85 + 21 \div (-3)] \times \dfrac{3}{8}$

12. (a) Round the following numbers to the nearest integer.

    (i) 4,562.4   **(ii)** 642.8

    (iii) 0.35   **(iv)** 199.5

(b) Round the following numbers to the nearest 10.

    (i) 38   **(ii)** 794

    (iii) 8,926   **(iv)** 995

(c) Round the following numbers to the nearest 100.

    (i) 51   **(ii)** 163

    (iii) 4,349   **(iv)** 950

13. (a) Round the following numbers to 1 decimal place.

    (i) 5.42   **(ii)** 31.16

    (iii) 68.68   **(iv)** 9.95

(b) Round the following numbers to 2 decimal places.

    (i) 3.142   **(ii)** 54.129

    (iii) 67.565   **(iv)** 9.995

(c) Round the following numbers to 3 decimal places.

    (i) 2.7183   **(ii)** 8.6567

    (iii) 65.2345   **(iv)** 4.9995

14. (a) Round 86,265 mm to the nearest

    (i) cm,   **(ii)** 10 cm,

    (iii) m.

(b) Round 59,485.69 g to the nearest

    (i) 1 decimal place,   **(ii)** 10 g,

    (iii) 100 g,   **(iv)** kg,

    (v) 10 kg.

15. If an integer is rounded to the nearest 10, it becomes 90.

(a) Write down all the possible values of the integer.

(b) List all the values in **(a)** which are prime numbers.

16. If an integer is rounded to the nearest 100, it becomes 2,800. Find

(a) the maximum possible value of the integer,

(b) the minimum possible value of the integer.

(Further Practice)

17. Describe the meaning of each of the following sentences.

(a) After a teacher graded Shirley's test paper again, the adjustment to her score is positive 4 points.

(b) The price of every hamburger sold in a particular food court was changed by positive 50 cents.

(c) The temperature of the conference room was adjusted by –3°C before the meeting.

(d) Keanu walked –100 meters due south from his house to the bus stop.

18. Find the missing number in each of the following.

(a) $3 \times (\quad) = -45$

(b) $(\quad) \div (-4) = 12$

(c) $3\frac{2}{9} + (\quad) = 10$

(d) $-15\frac{3}{5} + (\quad) = -7$

(e) $\sqrt{(\quad)} - 2 = 4$

(f) $1 + \sqrt[3]{(\quad)} = 3$

(g) $\sqrt[3]{(\quad)} - 2.5 = \frac{1}{2}$

19. Fill in the blanks with '>', '<', or '='.

(a) $2 \times [(-4)^3 - (-9)^2]$ _____ $(-5) \times 7$

(b) $-20 + 5 \times 9$ _____ $(-3)^2 + (-4)^2$

(c) $8^2 - 5 \times (10 \div 2)$ _____ $3^3 + 35 \div 7$

(d) $\frac{2}{21} \times \frac{7}{10}$ _____ $\frac{2}{3} \div \frac{8}{15} - 1$

(e) $\dfrac{\sqrt[3]{64}}{\sqrt{36}}$ _____ $\dfrac{\sqrt{9}}{\sqrt{25}} \div \dfrac{21}{20}$

20. Evaluate each of the following.

(a) $25 - |8|$

(b) $|-6| + 4$

(c) $|35 - 7|$

(d) $|8 - 23|$

(e) $|16| - |-5|$

(f) $|2(3) - 10| - |4(2) - 12|$

(g) $|4 - 3(6)| - |8 - 5(3)|$

21. Insert a pair of parentheses on the left-hand side of each of the following equalities to make the equality correct.

(a) $24 \div 2 \times 4 = 3$

(b) $30 - 4 + 5 - 5 = 16$

(c) $28 - 5 \times 2 + 1 = 13$

(d) $-36 \div 3 + 6 + 4 = 0$

(e) $6 + 36 \div 2 - 4 = 20$

(f) $3 \times 5 - 4 \times 2 = 22$

22 Evaluate each of the following.

(a) $4^3 \div 8^2 \div (-3)^2$

(b) $6^2 \div [25 - (-4)^2]$

(c) $[(-2)^3 + 4^3] \div 8 + 5$

(d) $8^2 - [1 + 5 \times (-2)] + (-4)^2$

(e) $(-4) \times (-24 + 19)^2 + 5 \times 20$

(f) $4 \times [5 \times (-2) + 10] \div (-5)$

(g) $\{[(-9)^2 + (-4)^3] + 51\} \div 4$

(h) $3 \times (-6)^2 \div (-2)^2 + (-3)^3$

23. Evaluate each of the following, giving your answers in the simplest form.

(a) $\frac{9}{24} \times \frac{8}{15} \div 13\frac{1}{2}$

(b) $\left(2\frac{1}{4} - 1\frac{1}{2} + \frac{1}{8}\right)^2$

(c) $\frac{1}{12} - \frac{3}{14} \div \frac{4}{7} + \left(\frac{1}{2}\right)^3$

(d) $\left(\frac{2}{5} - \frac{4}{10} + \frac{1}{4}\right) \div \left(\frac{3}{4} - \frac{1}{5} + \frac{1}{2}\right)$

(e) $\left[\left(-\frac{5}{8}\right)^2 - \left(\frac{3}{4}\right)^3\right] \times \frac{2}{3}$

(f) $\left(-\frac{4}{15}\right) \times \frac{1}{24} - \left(-\frac{1}{21}\right) \div \frac{2}{7}$

(g) $\left(-\frac{2}{21}\right) \div \frac{3}{14} + \frac{5}{8} \times \frac{24}{75}$

24. Evaluate each of the following as a rational number in its simplest form.

(a) $\dfrac{0.25}{2} + \dfrac{0.75}{3}$

(b) $\dfrac{0.5}{0.75} - \dfrac{0.64}{0.8}$

(c) $\dfrac{0.7}{3.5} + \dfrac{1.1}{4.5}$

(d) $\dfrac{\sqrt[3]{\dfrac{4^2}{0.25}}}{0.2}$

25. (a) Arrange $\dfrac{9}{11}, \dfrac{10}{13}$, and $\dfrac{11}{15}$ in ascending order.

(b) Arrange $\dfrac{11}{7}, \dfrac{13}{8}$, and $\dfrac{17}{11}$ in descending order.

26. Evaluate each of the following using a calculator.

(a) $\sqrt{66.25 - \left(1\dfrac{1}{2}\right)^2}$

(b) $(2.5^3 - 4.5^2)^3 \times [-(2^3)]^3$

(c) $\dfrac{\sqrt[3]{5\dfrac{5}{8} - 2\dfrac{1}{4}}}{\dfrac{1}{200}}$

(d) $\left(-\dfrac{4}{5}\right)^2 \div \left(\dfrac{2}{5}\right)^3 + \sqrt[3]{\dfrac{3}{8} - \dfrac{23}{64}}$

(e) $\dfrac{45 - \sqrt{35}}{45 + \sqrt{35}}$

(f) $\sqrt{8.5^3 - \dfrac{24^2}{5}}$

(g) $\dfrac{26.5^3 - \sqrt{5,000}}{\sqrt[3]{45,000}}$

27. (a) Express each of the following rational numbers as a repeating decimal.

(i) $\dfrac{31}{90}$

(ii) $\dfrac{7}{45}$

(iii) $1\dfrac{8}{15}$

(iv) $2\dfrac{5}{9}$

(b) Hence, round each of the rational numbers in **(a)** to 3 decimal places.

28. (a) Evaluate $3,463 \times 897.58$ using a calculator.

(b) Round your answer in **(a)** to

(i) 1 decimal place,

(ii) the nearest integer,

(iii) the nearest 10,

(iv) the nearest million.

29. Evaluate each of the following without the use of a calculator, giving your answers correct to 3 decimal places.

(a) $\dfrac{2}{3} + 2\dfrac{1}{4} - \left(1\dfrac{7}{10}\right)^2$

(b) $\dfrac{\sqrt{25^2 - 24^2}}{\sqrt{12^2 + 5^2}}$

(c) $3\dfrac{3}{7} \times \dfrac{1}{9} \div \dfrac{5}{14}$

(d) $6\dfrac{1}{3} - \dfrac{2}{9} \div 1\dfrac{1}{3}$

(e) $-2\dfrac{1}{9} + 1\dfrac{7}{8} \times \dfrac{2}{9}$

30. **(a)** Use a calculator to evaluate 5.228×87.751, giving your answer correct to 3 decimal places.
  (b) Estimate each of the following correct to the nearest integer.
    (i) 52.28×877.51
    (ii) 522.8×0.87751

Challenging Practice

31. During school-going days in a week, Lisa is usually given $5 as allowance daily. The table below shows the changes in her daily allowance for a particular week.

Day	Monday	Tuesday	Wednesday	Thursday	Friday
Change from the usual amount ($)	−1.5	1	−1.5	2	1.5

  (a) On which days did Lisa receive less than her usual daily allowance?
  (b) How much allowance did Lisa receive on Friday?
  (c) For the particular week, did Lisa receive more than, less than, or the same amount of weekly allowance compared to a usual week? Explain your answer.

32. The foot of a mountain is at sea level. On a particular afternoon, the temperatures at the foot and at the summit of the mountain are 10°C and −6°C respectively.
  (a) Calculate the drop in temperature from the foot to the summit of the mountain.
  (b) Suppose that the temperature drops by 6.4°C for every 1,000 m above sea level. How high, in km, is the mountain above sea level?

33. Suppose that Anthia cut out $\frac{5}{14}$ of a cake for herself, Harris took $\frac{2}{3}$ of the remaining portion, and Leo was given the rest.
  (a) Express the portion of the cake that was given to Leo as a rational number in its simplest form.
  (b) Identify the person who had the biggest portion of the cake.

34. A coastal patrol boat moved out from a naval base at 8 P.M. It patrolled eastwards for 21 km, westwards for 15 km and then eastwards for 6 km before turning off its engine. Suppose that throughout the patrol, the boat moved at 30 km an hour.
  (a) How far away and in what direction was the boat from the naval base when it stopped?
  (b) How long, in hours and minutes, did the boat move before stopping?
  (c) At what time did the boat stop?

35. Mr. Lewis and Mr. Baker are businessmen who each claims himself to be the richer of the two. Suppose that Mr. Lewis has 6^{12} while Mr. Baker has 7^{11}.
  (a) Use a calculator to determine who is richer, Mr. Lewis or Mr. Baker.
  (b) How much more money does the richer person have?

36. The prices of selected items sold in a supermarket are given in the table below.

Item	Unit	Unit Price
Olive oil	Bottle	$23.95
Oranges	Number	$0.54
Soft Drink	Can	$0.98

Linda wants to buy 2 bottles of olive oil, 8 oranges, and a dozen cans of soft drink.
(a) Estimate her total bill by rounding the unit price of each item to the nearest 10 cents.
(b) Is it possible for Linda to pay for her purchases with the amount estimated in **(a)**? Explain your answer.

Enrichment

37. (a) Find the values of the following.
   (i) $|7|$
   (ii) $|-5|$
   (iii) $|8-9|$
   (iv) $|-3 \times 2|$

(b) Find the value of $\dfrac{|a|}{a}$ when
   (i) $a > 0$,
   (ii) $a < 0$.

(c) Is $|x + y| = |x| + |y|$ for any two numbers x and y? Explain briefly.

38. In each of the following, add the operators $+, -, \times, \div$, and/or parentheses at appropriate places so that both sides are equal.
   (a) 0.6   0.6   0.6   0.6   0.6 = 0
   (b) 0.6   0.6   0.6   0.6   0.6 = 1
   (c) 0.6   0.6   0.6   0.6   0.6 = 2
   (d) 0.6   0.6   0.6   0.6   0.6 = 3
   (e) 0.6   0.6   0.6   0.6   0.6 = 4

39. Find the values of the following without using a calculator.
   (a) $1{,}690 \times 3.7 + (-169) \times (-61) - (-16.9) \times 20$
   (b) $(-16.28) \times (-6.53) - 9.28 \times 6.53 - 2.47 \times (-5.09) - (-2.47) \times 1.91$

40. (a) Express $\dfrac{1}{7}, \dfrac{2}{7}, \dfrac{3}{7}, \dfrac{4}{7}, \dfrac{5}{7}$, and $\dfrac{6}{7}$ as decimals.

(b) Describe some properties of the decimal representation of the fractions in **(a)**.

(c) Show that $\dfrac{2}{9} = 0.\overline{2}$.

(d) Using the results in **(a)** and **(c)**, express $\dfrac{3}{7} + \dfrac{2}{9}$ as a decimal.

41. A ream of A4 paper has 500 sheets. Its dimensions are measured to be 29.5 cm long, 21.0 cm wide, and 4.8 cm thick.

   (a) Describe the degree of accuracy of the measurements.

   (b) To calculate the area of a sheet of paper,

> Anthony's working is: $29.5 \times 21.0 = 619.5$
> $= 620 \text{ cm}^2$ (correct to the nearest integer);
>
> Mary's working is: $29.5 \times 21.0 = 30 \times 21$ (correct to the nearest integer)
> $= 630 \text{ cm}^2$ (correct to the nearest integer)

      Determine who is correct. Explain briefly.

   (c) Find the thickness of a sheet of paper and state the degree of accuracy.

   (d) Can we measure the thickness of a sheet of paper directly by an ordinary ruler? Explain briefly.

42. (a) Clive wants to paint the walls of a rectangular room which are 5.26 m long, 4.17 m wide, and 2.85 m high. Find the total area of the walls of the room, correct to the nearest square meter. (Assume there are no windows and doors in the room.)

   (b) Paint is sold in cubical cans of 3.468 liters each. One liter of paint can cover 12 m^2 of a wall. How many cans should Clive buy?

   (c) Estimate the length of a side of the tin in **(b)** correct to the nearest cm.

3 Introduction To Algebra

1. Simplify the following.
   (a) $(2w)^2$
   (b) $3p \times 4p$
   (c) $3q^2 \times 5q$
   (d) $2r \times (4r)^2$
   (e) $12x^2 \div 4$
   (f) $24y^3 \div 2y$
   (g) $21w^2 \div 7w^2$
   (h) $18z^2 \div (3z)^2$

2. Simplify the following.
   (a) $2x \times 3y$
   (b) $18y \div 3x$
   (c) $6x \div 2y \times 3w$
   (d) $8y \times 3y \div 2x$
   (e) $p \times 5q - 2 \times 3r$
   (f) $3x + 8y \div 2z$
   (g) $(3p)^2 + 5q \times 2r$
   (h) $(5b)^2 - 3c \times 2d$

3. When $x = 3$ and $y = 5$, evaluate the following expressions.
   (a) $4x - 5y$
   (b) $8y + 2x$
   (c) $3y^2 + (2x)^2$
   (d) $2y^3 - (2x)^3$
   (e) $\dfrac{x}{y}$
   (f) $\dfrac{4x}{y^2}$
   (g) $\dfrac{x + y}{x - y}$
   (h) $\dfrac{x^2 + y^2}{(x - y)^3}$

4. When $x = -2$, $y = -5$, and $z = 3$, evaluate the following expressions.
   (a) $2.5x - 3y + 4z$
   (b) $3x + \dfrac{2z}{y}$
   (c) $3xy - yz$
   (d) $2y \times (z^2 - xy)$
   (e) $x^2 + y^2 + z^2$
   (f) $\dfrac{2x^3}{(z + y)^2}$
   (g) $x^3 + y^3 + z^3$
   (h) $-3x^3 - y^3 + \dfrac{1}{9}z^3$

5. Find the value of
   (a) $\sqrt[3]{\dfrac{2p}{q}}$ when $p = 16$ and $q = \dfrac{1}{2}$,
   (b) $p(R^2 - r^2)$ when $p = \dfrac{22}{7}$, $R = 25$, and $r = 24$,
   (c) kx^t when $k = 5$, $x = 7$, and $t = 2$,
   (d) $(kx + 2y)^z$ when $k = 3.5$, $x = 4$, $y = -5$, and $z = 3$,
   (e) $\dfrac{k}{(\sqrt{x})^3}$ when $k = 3$ and $x = \dfrac{1}{4}$,
   (f) $\sqrt{\dfrac{1}{a} + \dfrac{1}{b} + \dfrac{1}{c}}$ when $a = \dfrac{1}{21}$, $b = -\dfrac{1}{5}$, and $c = \dfrac{1}{9}$.

6. Express the following word statements algebraically.
   (a) Subtract $3x$ from the sum of $4y$ and z.
   (b) Add $5r$ to the quotient of $2s$ divided by t.
   (c) Multiply the square of x to the cube of y.
   (d) Divide the sum of f and the square root of g by h.
   (e) Square the quotient of a divided by c.
   (f) Add p squared and q cubed to the product of m and n.

7. Simon bought x chairs at \$15 each. He also bought y tables at \$24 each.
   (a) Express the total cost of x chairs and y tables in terms of x and y.
   (b) Hence, evaluate the total cost of 4 chairs and 7 tables.

8. The length and width of a rectangle are $5l$ cm and $2b$ cm respectively. Express, in terms of l and b,
   (a) the perimeter of the rectangle,
   (b) the area of the rectangle.

9. Alvin's present age is 4 years less than 3 times the present age of Sylvester. If Sylvester is x years old now, express, in terms of x,
   (a) Alvin's present age,
   (b) Alvin's age in 5 years' time.

10. Frank is twice as heavy as Nelson now. If Nelson's mass is w kg now, express, in terms of w,
    (a) Frank's mass now,
    (b) Frank's mass 2 months ago if he is 1500 g heavier now compared to 2 months ago.

Further Practice

11. Given that $x = 5$ and $y = 128$, find the value of $\sqrt[3]{25x} + \sqrt{\dfrac{y}{2}}$.

12. (a) Simplify $(3a)^3 - (4b)^2$.
    (b) Given that $x = -2$, $y = -8$, and $z = \dfrac{1}{4}$, find the value of each of the following.
       (i) $\left(xz - \dfrac{x}{y} \right)^2$
       (ii) $\dfrac{z}{x} + \dfrac{x}{y} + \dfrac{y}{z}$

13. Given that $x = 2$, $y = -3$, and $z = -1$, find the value of each of the following.
    (a) $(5xyz)^2 - 5(x + yz)^2$
    (b) $12yz - \dfrac{(y - x)^2}{xy}$

14. Given that $a = 5$, $b = -4$, $c = 1$, and $d = -3$, find the value of each of the following.

   (a) $\dfrac{a - \sqrt{d^2 + 11a}}{abcd}$

   (b) $\dfrac{(a - b)^2 + (c - d)^2}{\sqrt{b^2 + d^2}}$

15. A car salesman's total monthly salary consists of a basic salary of \$$b$ and a commission of \$900 for every car that he sells.

   (a) In a particular month, the salesman sold n cars. Express his total salary for that month in terms of b and n.

   (b) Calculate his total salary over a 1-year period if his basic monthly salary is \$450 and he sells 4 cars every month.

16. The total monthly cost of running a factory is \$$(800x + 4,500)$, where x is the number of odd job workers employed.

   (a) Find the cost of running the factory in a particular month in which 15 odd job workers were employed.

   (b) Give a possible interpretation of the numbers 800 and 4,500.

17. The cost of polishing the two sides of a triangular panel is \$$\left(\dfrac{3}{4}xy\right)$, where x and y are the length and the height of the triangular panel respectively in meters.

   (a) Express, in terms of x and y, the cost of polishing 64 such triangular panels.

   (b) **(i)** Express, in terms of x and y, the total surface area of the two sides of the panel.

   (ii) Hence, find the cost of polishing every square meter of a panel.

18. A toy car moves x cm every second for the first 13 seconds. For the next $\dfrac{1}{5}$ minute, the toy car moves y cm every second.

   (a) Express, in terms of x and y, the total distance, in cm, moved by the toy car during the first 13 seconds and the next $\dfrac{1}{5}$ minute.

   (b) The average speed, S, of an object is defined by the formula $S = \dfrac{\text{total distance}}{\text{total time}}$.

   (i) Formulate and write down an expression for the average speed of the toy car during the first 13 seconds and the next $\dfrac{1}{5}$ minute in centimeters per second.

   (ii) Hence, find the average speed of the toy car in centimeters per second if the car moves 20 cm every second for the first 13 seconds and 30 cm every second for the next $\dfrac{1}{5}$ minute.

19. There are m ducks and n goats in a farm. The selling price of a duck is \$$x$ and the selling price of a goat is \$$y$.

   (a) How many legs do m ducks and n goats have altogether?

   (b) How much money can m ducks and n goats sell for?

   (c) The number of ducks in the farm is 20 more than 4 times the number of goats. A goat sells for \$5 less than 10 times the selling price of a duck. If there are 85 goats in the farm and each duck sells for \$8, how much money can all the ducks and all the goats sell for?

20. The amount of kinetic energy, E, in any moving object can be expressed by the formula $E = \frac{1}{2}MV^2$ where M is the mass and V is the speed of the object.

The mass and speed of object A is m units and v units respectively. Suppose that the mass of object B is 5 units less than 2 times the mass of A and the speed of object B is half the speed of A.

(a) Express, in terms of m and v, the amount of kinetic energy in object B.

(b) Calculate the amount of kinetic energy in object B if the mass of object A is 20 units and its speed is 18 units.

(**Challenging Practice**)

21. Angelica bought x bags of apples from a fruit seller at a total cost of $\$y$. Each bag is packed with z apples.

(a) Express the cost of each apple in terms of x, y, and z.

(b) Upon returning home, Angelica realized that she left 2 bags of apples on a bus. She also discarded w rotten apples, washed, and repacked the remaining good apples equally into the x bags. Express, in terms of w, x, y, and z,

    (i) the total cost of all the apples that were either left on the bus or were rotten,

    (ii) the number of good apples Angelica took home,

    (iii) the number of good apples in each bag after repacking.

22. A ball is dropped from a point P that is above ground level. The height of the ball, h meters, above ground level t seconds after the ball is dropped is given by $h = -5t^2 + 45$ for $0 \leqslant t \leqslant 3$.

(a) Find the height of the ball above the ground level after 2 seconds.

(b) Deduce and write down the height of the point P above the ground level.

(c) Hence, find the distance between the ball and P after 2 seconds.

23. The cost of m bars of chocolate and n packs of cookies are $\$d$ and $\$e$ respectively.

(a) Express, in terms of d, e, m and n,

    (i) the cost of one bar of chocolate,

    (ii) the cost of one pack of cookies,

    (iii) the total cost of three bars of chocolate and five packs of cookies.

(b) Suppose the cost of each bar of chocolate is increased by 10 cents and the price of each pack of cookies is decreased by 5 cents. Express the total cost of three bars of chocolate and five packs of cookies in terms of d, e, m, and n.

24. A piece of cucumber is x cm long. Mrs. Taylor removes y cm of it from each end. The remaining piece is chopped into n small pieces of equal thickness along the length of the cucumber.

(a) Express the thickness of each small piece in terms of n, x, and y.

(b) When $n = 8$, $x = 26$, and $y = 1$, find the thickness of each small piece.

(c) Do you think the mass of each small piece is the same? Explain briefly.

25. For a positive integer n, **n factorial**, denoted by $n!$, is the product of the first n consecutive integers.

i.e., $\qquad n! = n \times (n-1) \times (n-2) \times \ldots \times 3 \times 2 \times 1.$

For example, $\quad 4! = 4 \times 3 \times 2 \times 1 = 24;$
$\qquad\qquad\quad 7! = 7 \times 6 \times 5 \times 4 \times 3 \times 2 \times 1 = 5{,}040.$

(a) Find the value of each of the following.
  (i) $5!$
  (ii) $8!$
  (iii) $10!$
  (iv) $\dfrac{100!}{98!}$

(b) What is the relation between $n!$ and $(n-1)!$?

Enrichment

26. Note that $\qquad \dfrac{1}{1 \times 2} + \dfrac{1}{2 \times 3} = \left(1 - \dfrac{1}{2}\right) + \left(\dfrac{1}{2} - \dfrac{1}{3}\right)$

$$= 1 - \dfrac{1}{3}$$

$$= \dfrac{2}{3}.$$

(a) Use the same method to calculate

  (i) $\dfrac{1}{1 \times 2} + \dfrac{1}{2 \times 3} + \dfrac{1}{3 \times 4},$

  (ii) $\dfrac{1}{1 \times 2} + \dfrac{1}{2 \times 3} + \dfrac{1}{3 \times 4} + \dfrac{1}{4 \times 5}.$

(b) Suggest a formula for the sum $\dfrac{1}{1 \times 2} + \dfrac{1}{2 \times 3} + \dfrac{1}{3 \times 4} + \ldots + \dfrac{1}{n(n+1)}$, where n is a positive integer.

(c) Hence, find the value of $\dfrac{1}{1 \times 2} + \dfrac{1}{2 \times 3} + \dfrac{1}{3 \times 4} + \ldots + \dfrac{1}{100 \times 101}.$

27. (a) Complete the following table.

n	1	2	3	4	5	6
$n(n+5)$						
$(n-3)(n+2)$						
$n(n+5) - (n-3)(n+2)$						

(b) Describe a property of the number $n(n+5) - (n-3)(n+2)$, where n is a positive integer.

28. (a) Complete the following table.

n	1	2	3	4	5
$n^2 + n$					
$\dfrac{n^2 + n}{n}$					

(b) If n is a positive integer, express $n^2 + n$ as a product of two positive integers.

(c) There is a square tile pattern of n by n tiles and a row of n tiles. All the tiles are of the same size. If the row of n tiles is joined to the square pattern to form a rectangular pattern, what are the dimensions of the rectangle?

(d) If there are 2,256 pieces of tiles in the rectangular pattern in **(c)**, find the value of n.

4 Algebraic Manipulation

1. Simplify each of the following.
   (a) $5x + 7x$
   (b) $3y - 10y$
   (c) $-12y - 6y + 9y$
   (d) $2 \times 3w + 8w$
   (e) $-5m + (-4) \times 3m$
   (f) $4a \times 3b - 9ab$
   (g) $20xy + 5xy - 16xy$
   (h) $30st + 3s \times (-7t) - 4t \times 2s$

2. Simplify each of the following.
   (a) $(2d + 1) + (4d + 5)$
   (b) $(3e + 4) + (-7 + 2e)$
   (c) $(7f - 2) - (6f + 12)$
   (d) $(3g + 10) - (9g + 10)$
   (e) $(4x - 6y) + (5x - 8y)$
   (f) $(-11j + 9k) - (15k - 11j)$
   (g) $(12p + q) + (12p - q)$
   (h) $(10m + 3n) - (3n + m)$

3. Expand each of the following.
   (a) $2(5 + x)$
   (b) $-3(2x + 7)$
   (c) $(3f - 5g)(4)$
   (d) $\frac{3}{2}(10x + 8y - 6z)$
   (e) $(25f - 15g)\left(-\frac{1}{5}\right)$
   (f) $4p(7 + 3q)$
   (g) $-w(3x - 4y)$
   (h) $5a(2b - 3c + d)$
   (i) $\left(\frac{27}{4}r\right)\left(\frac{8}{9}s + \frac{16}{3}t\right)$
   (j) $\left(-\frac{3}{5}w\right)(-20x + 5y)$

4. Simplify each of the following.
   (a) $2(8 + 3q) + 3(4q + 5)$
   (b) $5(3x - 4) - 6(2x + 3)$
   (c) $4(-2 + 5y) + 2(4 - 3y)$
   (d) $\frac{3}{2}(4c + 6) - \frac{2}{5}(15c - 30)$
   (e) $-\frac{1}{3}(1 + 6p) + \frac{1}{2}\left(6p - \frac{4}{3}\right)$
   (f) $3(a + 4b) + 4(2a - 3b)$
   (g) $-4(p + 3q) + 2(5p - 3q)$
   (h) $5(-2r + 5s) - 3(4s - 7r)$
   (i) $3(3x - 5y - 2) - 2(7 + 5x - 8y)$
   (j) $\frac{n}{4}(8m - 12) - \frac{m}{3}(6n - 9)$

5. Simplify the expressions where necessary and then find the coefficient of x in each of the following.
   (a) $2x^2 + 3x - 12$
   (b) $3xy + 3xz - 2x + 8$
   (c) $(10x - 9y) - (7y - 2x)$
   (d) $10\left(6x^2 - \frac{1}{2}x + 4\right)$
   (e) $5(-6x + 2y) + 3(4y + 3x)$
   (f) $-4(3x + 9) - 2x(x + 2)$
   (g) $\frac{7}{2}(4x - 6w) - \frac{x}{3}(6 + 9x)$
   (h) $2(4x^2 - 7x - 8y) - 5(6x^2 - 5x + 12y) + x$

6. **(a)** Simplify the expressions where necessary and then find the coefficient of xy in each of the following.
   (i) $3x^2 - xy + 3y - 4$
   (ii) $4xy + xy^2 - 7xy + 2x + 3y$
   (iii) $9x^2y - 4xy + 5yx + 7$
   (iv) $4\left(y^2 - \dfrac{3}{2} + 2xy\right)$
   (v) $5(-xy + y) - 2x(y - x) + y(x + y)$
   (vi) $3(3xy + 2y) + 2y(-4x + 5y) - 7x(2x + 3y)$

   (b) Simplify the expressions where necessary and then find the constant term in each of the following.
   (i) $3y^2 + 3y - 11$
   (ii) $3(-4 + 2x) + 2(6y + 7)$
   (iii) $3w(1 + 8x) - 2(6w - 5)$

7. Factor each of the following.
   (a) $4c + 8$
   (b) $10 - 6d$
   (c) $-6m + 9$
   (d) $-12 - 18n$
   (e) $28y + 7x$
   (f) $20p - 5q$
   (g) $-15m + 9n$
   (h) $-4x - 12y$
   (i) $30ab + 45a$
   (j) $18y - 27xy$

8. Factor each of the following.
   (a) $3w(2x + y) + (2x + y)$
   (b) $a(4b - 3c) - 2d(4b - 3c)$
   (c) $4p(7m - 5n) + 5q(-7m + 5n)$
   (d) $2c(9a + 2b) - 3d(-9a - 2b)$
   (e) $3 + 4t + 6s + 8st$
   (f) $5a - 6b + 30ac - 36bc$
   (g) $9ac + 2bc + 9ad + 2bd$
   (h) $21xz + 24yz - 14x - 16y$
   (i) $4hj - 14hk - 10gj + 35gk$
   (j) $6ac - 2ad - 15bc + 5bd$
   (k) $-15mp - 20np + 9mq + 12nq$

9. Express each of the following in its simplest form.
   (a) $\dfrac{x + 1}{2} + \dfrac{3x + 4}{2}$
   (b) $\dfrac{2y - 5}{3} + \dfrac{5y + 7}{3}$
   (c) $\dfrac{6w + 4}{5} - \dfrac{1 - 3w}{5}$
   (d) $\dfrac{-3 + 5x}{4} - \dfrac{x - 1}{4}$
   (e) $\dfrac{3z - 7}{2} - \dfrac{5z + 3}{2}$
   (f) $\dfrac{8y - 3x}{4} + \dfrac{-7y + 5x}{4}$
   (g) $\dfrac{-2p + 5q}{6} - \dfrac{8q - 2p}{6}$
   (h) $\dfrac{a + 10b}{3} - \dfrac{b - 5a}{3}$

10. Simplify and express each of the following in terms of n.
   (a) The sum of 3 consecutive integers if the value of the smallest integer is $n + 1$.
   (b) The sum of 3 consecutive even integers if the value of the middle integer is $2n$.
   (c) The sum of 3 consecutive odd integers if the value of the largest integer is $3n - 4$.
   (d) The length of a side of a square whose perimeter is $(24n + 8)$ cm.

11. (a) Find the sum of
    (i) $8x + 15y$ and $6x - 10y$,
    (ii) $7a - 3b, -4a + 9b$, and $-9a - 10b$,
    (iii) $2(4p - 5q)$ and $3(-4q + 3p)$,
    (iv) $\frac{1}{4}$ of $(8x - 12y)$ and $\frac{3}{2}$ of $(4x + 10y)$.

(b) Subtract
    (i) $4s + 9t$ from $3s - t$,
    (ii) $8r - 5w$ from $7w + 12r$,
    (iii) $-\frac{2}{3}(3x + 9y)$ from $\frac{1}{2}(8x + 14y)$.

(c) Subtract $7m - 8n$ from the sum of $7n - 8m$ and $20m - 9n$.

12. Simplify each of the following.
    (a) $(3m - 7) + 2(4m - 5n) - 3(1 - 2n)$
    (b) $(3a + 5b - 7) + (4a - 6b + 5)$
    (c) $(4p - 7q - 9) - (p + 5 + 3q)$
    (d) $\left(-\frac{1}{2}x + \frac{2}{3}y - \frac{3}{4}\right) - \left(\frac{3}{2}x - \frac{7}{3}y + \frac{1}{4}\right)$
    (e) $5(x + 4y - 1) + 4(-4x + 6y - 2)$
    (f) $-5(3p - 2q - 8) - 4(-10 + 3p - q)$
    (g) $3\left(\frac{1}{6}a + \frac{1}{4}b - 2\right) + 4\left(\frac{5}{8}a + \frac{9}{16}b - 1\right)$
    (h) $\frac{8}{5}\left(\frac{5}{2}s - \frac{3}{4}t - \frac{5}{8}\right) - \frac{2}{3}\left(12s + \frac{6}{5}t - 3\right)$

13. Simplify each of the following.
    (a) $4[-2a + 4 - 2(a + 3)]$
    (b) $6w - 5 + 3[(4 - 3w) - 2(w - 8)]$
    (c) $4 - 7c - 2[(c + 4) + 2(2c - 5)]$
    (d) $2s + 9 - 3(s - 5) - 2[3(3 - s) + 2(4 - 3s)]$
    (e) $3[5 - 3w - 5(2w + 1)]$
    (f) $-y + 3x + 2[3x - y + 2(y - 2x)]$
    (g) $4(3p + 7q) - 5[4p - (q + 4p) + 5q]$
    (h) $-21m + 8n - 3[2(m - 2n) - 3(3m - 2n)]$

14. (a) (i) Simplify the expression $3a + 9 - 5a - 6$.
    (ii) Hence, find the value of the expression when $a = 2.5$.
  (b) (i) Simplify the expression $2(4b - 7c) - 3(2c - 3b)$.
    (ii) Hence, find the value of the expression when $b = -6$ and $c = \frac{1}{2}$.
  (c) (i) Simplify the expression $\frac{x}{3}(6y - 9) - \frac{x}{2}(8y - 6)$.
    (ii) Hence, find the value of the expression when $x = 5$ and $y = -3$.
  (d) (i) Simplify the expression $\frac{3}{5}p - \frac{1}{4}q + \frac{3}{10}(2p - q)$.
    (ii) Hence, find the value of the expression when $p = 15$ and $q = -10$.
  (e) (i) Simplify the expression $40 - z - 3[2(4 + 3z) - 3(3z - 1)]$.
    (ii) Hence, find the value of the expression when $z = 4$.

15. Express each of the following in its simplest form.
    (a) $\frac{2x + 1}{3} + \frac{x - 3}{4}$
    (b) $\frac{4y - 3}{3} - \frac{y - 5}{2}$
    (c) $\frac{4z + 2}{4} + \frac{1 - 5z}{5}$
    (d) $\frac{3(2 - 3w)}{2} + \frac{6(4w - 3)}{5}$
    (e) $\frac{3(4p + 5)}{5} - \frac{2(3p + 1)}{3}$
    (f) $\frac{q + 5}{2} + \frac{2q + 7}{5} - 1$
    (g) $\frac{2(2p - q)}{3} - \frac{3(q + 4p)}{2} + \frac{1}{4}$
    (h) $12\left(\frac{m + 2n}{3} - \frac{m - 3n}{6} + \frac{m + n}{2}\right)$

16. Factor each of the following.
  (a) $6a + 4b - 12$
  (b) $8 - 3(2s + 4t)$
  (c) $9a - 18b - 15c$
  (d) $8pq + 16p + 24pq$
  (e) $15xy - (21 + 27z)x$
  (f) $2w(3x - 4y) + 8wz$
  (g) $20ps - 3s(8q - 10r)$
  (h) $-4(2f + g) - \dfrac{2}{3}(6g + 18h)$

17. Factor each of the following.
  (a) $5 - 5a + ab - b$
  (b) $2qr - 4r + 14 - 7q$
  (c) $6a + 5bc - 2c - 15ab$
  (d) $ac + 2bd - 2ad - bc$
  (e) $21ax - 8by + 6bx - 28ay$
  (f) $20mq - 15np - 12nq + 25mp$
  (g) $9wx - 2yz + 6wy - 3xz$

18. (a) (i) Factor $8p - 24pq + 16$.
      (ii) Then, find the value of the expression when $p = 3$ and $q = -1$.
   (b) (i) Factor $3f - 12fh - 4g + 16gh$.
      (ii) Then, find the value of the expression when $f = \dfrac{2}{3}$, $g = -3$, and $h = -1$.
   (c) (i) Factor $3w(3x - 4y) - (-3x + 4y)$.
      (ii) Then, find the value of the expression when $w = 3$, $x = \dfrac{2}{3}$, and $y = -\dfrac{1}{2}$.
   (d) (i) Factor $a - 12bc - 2b + 6ac$.
      (ii) Then, find the value of the expression when $a = 3$, $b = -2$, and $c = 2$.

19. Compute the following without using a calculator.
  (a) $88 \times 34 + 12 \times 34$
  (b) $243 \times 0.87 + 0.13 \times 243$
  (c) $59 \times 58 + 59 \times (-48)$
  (d) $-44.5 \times 99 + 99 \times (-55.5)$
  (e) $123 \times 78 - 23 \times 78$
  (f) $458 \times 0.56 - 0.46 \times 458$
  (g) $94 \times (-61) - 94 \times 39$
  (h) $31 \times 267 - 267 \times (-69)$

20. (a) Show that the expression $\dfrac{4x - 3}{2} - \dfrac{2(x + 3)}{3} - \dfrac{8x - 1}{6}$ does not depend on x.
   (b) (i) Factor $2tx + y + 2ty + x$.
      (ii) Hence, show that factors of $2tx + y + 2ty + x$ must be odd if $x + y$ is odd and t, x, and y are positive integers.
      (iii) Factor $8st - 3 - 4s + 6t$.
      (iv) Hence, show that possible factors of $8st - 3 - 4s + 6t$ are odd if s and t are integers.

Challenging Practice

21. Jasmine is n years old now. Jasmine's brother, Eddie is 3 years younger than 2 times her age. The sum of their parents' ages is 1 year more than 3 times the sum of their ages.
   (a) Simplify, in terms of n,
      (i) Eddie's age,
      (ii) the sum of the parents' ages,
      (iii) the sum of the ages of Jasmine, Eddie, and their parents.
   (b) If $n = 9$, find the sum of the ages of
      (i) Jasmine, Eddie, and their parents now,
      (ii) Jasmine, Eddie, and their parents 4 years later.

22. Last year, Sheryl borrowed $(6x + 12y)$ books from the library. Murray borrowed $\frac{2}{3}$ as many books as Sheryl and Lina borrowed $\frac{1}{2}$ as many books as Murray.

(a) Find, in terms of x and y, the number of books borrowed by
  (i) Murray,
  (ii) Lina.

(b) Hence, find the total number of books borrowed by Sheryl, Murray, and Lina in terms of x and y.

(c) If $x = 3$ and $y = \frac{1}{2}$, find the total number of books borrowed by Sheryl, Murray, and Lina.

23. In a supermarket, fruit juice is sold in packs of 2 bottles or 5 bottles respectively. The table below shows the corresponding price of each pack.

Pack	Description of Item and Quantity	Price ($)
A	2 bottles of fruit juice	$4x + 10y - 3$
B	5 bottles of fruit juice	$15x + 25y - \frac{25}{2}$

(a) Express, in terms of x and y,
  (i) the price of 1 bottle of fruit juice in pack A,
  (ii) the price of 1 bottle of fruit juice in pack B.

(b) Does pack A or pack B offer a better value if $x = 4$? Explain your answer.

24. The length and width of a rectangle are $(2y + 1)$ cm and $3x$ cm respectively. The base and height of a triangle are $(7y + 1)$ cm and $2x$ cm respectively.

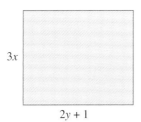   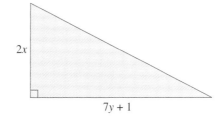

(a) Find, in terms of x and y,
  (i) the area of the rectangle,
  (ii) the area of the triangle.

(b) Subtract the area of the rectangle from the area of the triangle expressing your answer in terms of x and y.

(c) (i) Factor your answer in (b).
  (ii) If y is a prime number, show that the area of the triangle is always greater than or equal to the area of the rectangle.

25. Johnny and Marcus ran the same distance to determine who runs faster. Their coach recorded the time taken by each of them to complete the distance. Suppose that the time taken by Johnny subtracted from the time taken by Marcus is $(2xy - 5y - 15 + 6x)$ seconds.

(a) Factor $2xy - 5y - 15 + 6x$.

(b) Given that y is positive and $x = 1.5$, determine who ran faster. Explain your answer.

26.

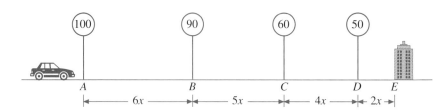

In the figure, *ABCDE* is a portion of a road from the exit *A* of an expressway to a building *E*. $AB = 6x$ km, $BC = 5x$ km, $CD = 4x$ km, and $DE = 2x$ km. A car drives at the speed limits, i.e., 100 km/hr, 90 km/hr, 60 km/hr, and 50 km/hr in each section from *A* to *E* respectively. Let *T* minutes be the time taken by the car to reach *E* from *A*.

(a) Express *T* in terms of *x*.

(b) When $x = 0.45$, find the value of *T*.

27. The sides of $\triangle ABC$ are $AB = (3x + 4)$ cm, $BC = (4x - 5)$ cm, and $CA = (x + 13)$ cm.

(a) Express the perimeter of $\triangle ABC$ in terms of *x*. Give the answer in factored form.

(b) A square *PQRS* has the same perimeter as $\triangle ABC$. Express the length of *PQ* in terms of *x*.

(c) When $x = 7$, find
   (i) the perimeter of $\triangle ABC$,
   (ii) the area of *PQRS*.

28.

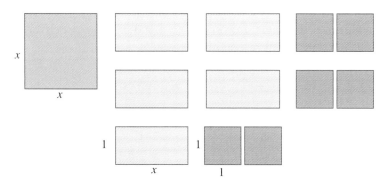

(a) The figure shows 1 square tile of *x* by *x* units, 5 rectangular tiles of *x* by 1 unit, and 6 square tiles of 1 by 1 unit. Arrange the tiles to form a rectangle and state its dimensions.

(b) Hence, or otherwise, express $x^2 + 5x + 6$ in the form $(x + a)(x + b)$, where *a* and *b* are integers.

(c) Express $x^2 + 8x + 15$ in the form $(x + p)(x + q)$, where *p* and *q* are integers.

29. The volumes of two glasses of water are $(7ax - 3bx + 6ay - 4by)$ cm³ and $(11bx + 5ax - 6by - 21ay)$ cm³ respectively. Let *V* cm³ be the total volume of water in the two glasses.

(a) Express *V* in terms of *a*, *b*, *x*, and *y* in factored form.

(b) If both *x* and *y* are doubled, determine whether *V* will be doubled.

5 Simple Equations In One Variable

Basic Practice

1. Solve the following equations.
   (a) $x + 12 = 17$
   (b) $x - 8 = 12$
   (c) $14 - x = 11$
   (d) $2x = 10$
   (e) $-3x = 27$
   (f) $\dfrac{x}{7} = 4$
   (g) $\dfrac{x}{5} = -9$
   (h) $\dfrac{x}{3} + 1 = -5$
   (i) $\dfrac{x}{4} - 3 = 17$
   (j) $20 - \dfrac{x}{7} = 18$

2. Solve the following equations.
   (a) $3c - 9 = -24$
   (b) $35 - 12w = 29$
   (c) $-4p - 45 = 15$
   (d) $3(2x + 5) = 45$
   (e) $5(2y - 9) = 60$
   (f) $-8(7 - 3z) = 64$
   (g) $2(5p + 14) = 3(1 - 5p)$
   (h) $3(2w - 11) = 5(6 - 3w)$
   (i) $7(2q - 5) - 4(7 - 4q) = 27$
   (j) $5(3m - 7) - 2(-8 + 7m) = 13 - 3(6 - 5m)$

3. (a) If $Y = 2X + 9$, find the value of X when $Y = 25$.
   (b) If $A = 8 - 3B$, find the value of B when $A = -22$.
   (c) If $T = \dfrac{S}{3} + 2$, find the value of S when $T = -9$.
   (d) If $P = 6 - \dfrac{Q}{4}$, find the value of Q when $P = 2.5$.
   (e) If $M = 3(2N - 5)$, find the value of N when $M = 18$.
   (f) If $K = -5(3T + 4) + 3(8 - 5T)$, find the value of T when $K = -6$.
   (g) If $W = \dfrac{1}{3}[4(6 - 5P) - 7(3P + 2)]$, find the value of P when $W = 17$.

4. Solve the following equations.
   (a) $\dfrac{4m + 5}{3} = 2m - 3$
   (b) $-7 + 6n = \dfrac{9n + 1}{2}$
   (c) $\dfrac{8(5 - 2q)}{3} = -7q + 10$
   (d) $\dfrac{4(7k - 2)}{5} - 2 = 2(3 + 2k)$
   (e) $\dfrac{3w - 1}{2} = \dfrac{4w + 5}{3}$
   (f) $\dfrac{5(3 - 4p)}{7} = \dfrac{7 - 3p}{2}$
   (g) $\dfrac{2(3x - 4)}{5} = \dfrac{-9 + 5x}{3}$
   (h) $\dfrac{4(23 - 80y)}{9} = \dfrac{7(10y + 13)}{2}$

5. Solve the following equations.

(a) $\dfrac{5}{x} = 4$

(b) $\dfrac{9}{x} = -3$

(c) $2 + \dfrac{7}{x} = -12$

(d) $9 - \dfrac{18}{x} = 45$

(e) $\dfrac{-14}{x - 10} = 2$

(f) $\dfrac{40}{x - 2} = -8$

(g) $\dfrac{7}{3(x + 5)} = \dfrac{1}{6}$

(h) $\dfrac{3}{5(1 - x)} = \dfrac{9}{10}$

6. (a) If $A = \dfrac{2B + 5}{4}$, find the value of B when $A = 5$.

(b) If $M = \dfrac{3(7 - 4N)}{5}$, find the value of N when $M = 21$.

(c) If $Y = \dfrac{5(2X - 1)}{3} - 7$, find the value of X when $Y = -12$.

(d) If $W = \dfrac{20}{x}$, find the value of x when $W = 4$.

(e) If $B = \dfrac{18}{y - 3}$, find the value of y when $B = -3$.

(f) If $K = -12 + \dfrac{10}{h - 4}$, find the value of h when $K = -17$.

(g) If $P = \dfrac{9}{2(z - 5)}$, find the value of z when $P = 4$.

7. The difference between 2 numbers is 110. The greater number is 5 more than 8 times the smaller number. Let the smaller number be n.
  (a) Express the greater number in terms of n.
  (b) Form an equation in terms of n and solve it.
  (c) Hence, find the
      (i) greater number,
      (ii) sum of the 2 numbers.

8. (a) The sum of 3 consecutive numbers is 234. Find the numbers.
  (b) The sum of 3 consecutive even numbers is 192. Find the numbers.
  (c) The sum of 3 consecutive odd numbers is 111. Find the numbers.

9. Dilbert is 12 cm taller than Jenny.
  (a) If Dilbert's height is x cm, express Jenny's height in terms of x.
  (b) Hence, find the height of Dilbert if Jenny's height is 156 cm.

10. Rudolf is 3 times as old as Mervin now and the sum of their present ages is 52. Let Mervin's present age be m.
  (a) Express Rudolf's present age in terms of m.
  (b) Form an equation in terms of m and solve it.
  (c) Hence, find the present age of Rudolf.

11. Solve the following equations.

    (a) $\dfrac{3}{8}w + \dfrac{15}{32} = 0$

    (b) $\dfrac{23}{2} - \dfrac{5}{7}z = 9$

    (c) $\dfrac{2}{3}a + \dfrac{1}{6} = -\dfrac{3}{2}$

    (d) $\dfrac{5}{4} - \dfrac{3}{10}b = -\dfrac{23}{20}$

    (e) $\dfrac{5}{18}c - \dfrac{2}{9} = \dfrac{3}{4}$

    (f) $3\left(\dfrac{4}{5}x - \dfrac{7}{2}\right) = 58.5$

    (g) $\dfrac{14}{5}\left(4 - \dfrac{2}{7}y\right) = 28$

12. Solve the following equations.

    (a) $\dfrac{w}{5} + 57 = -\dfrac{3}{4}w$

    (b) $\dfrac{x}{2} - \dfrac{2}{3} = -\dfrac{5}{6}x$

    (c) $\dfrac{7}{8}y - \dfrac{33}{2} + \dfrac{5}{4}y = \dfrac{y}{16}$

    (d) $\dfrac{5 - s}{2} - \dfrac{3s + 1}{5} = -1$

    (e) $\dfrac{2(1 + t)}{3} + \dfrac{2 + 3t}{4} = 4$

    (f) $\dfrac{5}{4}\left(8 - \dfrac{3n + 2}{25}\right) + 7 = \dfrac{36(1 + 2n)}{5}$

    (g) $\dfrac{2p + 1}{6} - \dfrac{6 - 5p}{5} = \dfrac{12p - 15}{10}$

    (h) $\dfrac{3 - 4m}{2} + \dfrac{7 - 2m}{4} - \dfrac{3m + 4}{5} = \dfrac{1}{8}$

13. (a) If $x = t(u + 5t)$, find the value of u when $x = 60$ and $t = 3$.

    (b) If $R = \dfrac{x^2 - ay}{3}$, find the value of y when $a = 7$, $x = -2$, and $R = 6$.

    (c) If $s = \dfrac{b}{3} - \dfrac{sc}{d}$, find the value of c when $b = 9$, $s = -12$, and $d = 4$.

    (d) If $T = P - \dfrac{3Q}{S}$, find the value of Q when $P = -6$, $S = -9$, and $T = -20$.

    (e) If $V = 3s - \dfrac{g}{s - t}$, find the value of g when $s = -5$, $t = -4\dfrac{2}{3}$, and $V = 9$.

    (f) If $\dfrac{B}{c} = 2c + \dfrac{4w}{a}$, find the value of w when $a = 2$, $c = \dfrac{1}{2}$, and $B = -5$.

    (g) If $\dfrac{1}{v} = \dfrac{3}{b} - \dfrac{t}{w}$, find the value of t when $b = \dfrac{1}{7}$, $w = -\dfrac{1}{6}$, and $v = \dfrac{2}{3}$.

14. Solve the following equations.

    (a) $\dfrac{7}{5s} = \dfrac{2}{s - 3}$

    (b) $\dfrac{3}{x - 2} = \dfrac{2}{x + 5}$

    (c) $\dfrac{4}{5 - y} = \dfrac{1}{2y - 1}$

    (d) $\dfrac{5}{-2 + 3z} = \dfrac{4}{2z - 3}$

    (e) $\dfrac{5p + 4}{3p + 4} = 7$

    (f) $\dfrac{2k - 7}{9k + 2} = -\dfrac{3}{20}$

    (g) $\dfrac{3w - 4}{5 - 4w} = -\dfrac{1}{2}$

    (h) $\dfrac{6 - 7z}{9 - 4z} = \dfrac{9}{7}$

15. (a) If $w = \dfrac{6 + 7x}{y}$, find the value of y when $x = 2$ and $w = 4$.

(b) If $S = \dfrac{3P - 4}{2t}$, find the value of t when $P = 8$ and $S = -5$.

(c) If $p = \dfrac{q + 1}{s + 3}$, find the value of s when $p = \dfrac{1}{4}$ and $q = 5$.

(d) If $K = \dfrac{g + 5}{r - 1}$, find the value of r when $g = -9$ and $K = 16$.

(e) If $P = \dfrac{r(q - 3)}{3m - 4}$, find the value of m when $q = 6\dfrac{1}{2}$, $r = -2$, and $P = -\dfrac{1}{2}$.

(f) If $z = 4w - \dfrac{3}{2s - a}$, find the value of s when $w = 2.5$, $a = -4$, and $z = 12$.

(g) If $\dfrac{y}{x} = 5w + \dfrac{3x}{2z - w}$, find the value of z when $w = -1$, $x = 2$, and $y = -8$.

16. In the diagram, $AB = (3x + 8)$ cm, $BC = \left(\dfrac{28}{2y - 1}\right)$ cm, $AC = \left(\dfrac{9x - 5}{2}\right)$ cm and $\triangle ABC$ is isosceles.

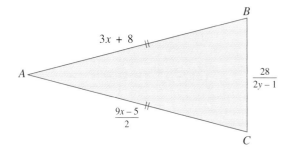

(a) Form an equation in terms of x and solve it.
(b) (i) Find the length of the side BC if the perimeter of the triangle is 72 cm.
    (ii) Hence, find the value of y.

17. Selina is 4 years younger than Kayden now. Three years ago, Selina's age was $\dfrac{3}{5}$ the age of Kayden then. Let the present age of Selina be w years old.
(a) Form an equation in terms of w and solve it.
(b) Hence, find Kayden's present age.

18. Elaine paid $10 for 6 pens and 8 erasers and was given $3.60 as change. Given that 2 pens cost $1 more than 3 erasers and each eraser costs $$x$,
(a) form an equation in terms of x and solve it,
(b) hence, find the cost of
    (i) each pen,
    (ii) 9 pens and 13 erasers.

19. The numerator of a fraction is 9 less than 2 times of its denominator. If 5 and 8 are added to the numerator and denominator respectively, the new fraction is equivalent to $\dfrac{2}{3}$. Find the original fraction.

20. Amanda thinks of a number x. She adds 5 to x and multiplies the sum by 2. If 56 is divided by the result, the final answer is -4. Find the number that Amanda thinks of using an algebraic method.

21. Mr. Jacob and Ms. Reese estimate that they will take 5 hours and 6 hours respectively to finish grading the same pile of books individually. If they grade the same pile of books together, the estimated time taken is x hours.
    (a) (i)   What fraction of the pile of books can Mr. Jacob finish grading in 1 hour?
        (ii) What fraction of the pile of books can Ms. Reese finish grading in 1 hour?
        (iii) What fraction of the same pile of books can both of them finish grading in 1 hour if they grade together?
    (b) (i)   Form an equation in terms of x and solve it.
        (ii) Hence, estimate, in hours and minutes, the time taken by Mr. Jacob and Ms. Reese to finish grading the pile of books together.

22. A and B are the starting and finishing points respectively of a 12-km cross-country route. At 07:00 A.M., Hendrick jogs from A towards B at 6 km/hr. At 07:30 A.M., Winnie strolls from B towards A at 3 km/hr.
    (a) At what time will Hendrick and Winnie meet?
    (b) How far would Hendrick have jogged when he meets Winnie?

23. 104 chickens and goats in a farm have 246 legs altogether. The selling price of a goat is $3 less than 11 times the selling price of a chicken. One chicken and one goat are sold for $93.
    (a) How many chickens and goats are there in the farm?
    (b) Find the price of each chicken and the price of each goat.
    (c) Hence, find the total receipt from selling all the chickens and goats in the farm.

24. An insurance company pays each of its agents a salary of P per month. The salary consists of a basic pay of $450 plus a commission of $700 for each of N new policies signed.
    (a) (i)   Express P in terms of N.
        (ii) Calculate the salary of an agent in a particular month in which 5 new policies were signed.
        (iii) If the salary of an agent was $2,550 in another month, find how many new policies were signed in that particular month.
    (b) Suppose that the insurance company decides to decrease the monthly basic pay of each of its agents by $\frac{2}{5}$ but increase the commission per new policy signed by $\frac{1}{10}$ plus an additional $20.
        (i)   Express P in terms of N for the new arrangement.
        (ii) Find how many new policies must be signed in a month for the agent to receive the same monthly salary under either arrangement.

25. Raymond and Wilson shared $350. The sum consists of a total of 19 ten-dollar and fifty-dollar bills. Let the number of ten-dollar bills be x.
    (a) Form an equation in terms of x and solve it.
    (b) Given that Wilson's share is $20 more than 2 times Raymond's share, find how much did each of them receive.
    (c) If the number of bills Wilson has is 2 less than 6 times the number of bills Raymond has, find the exact number of ten-dollar and fifty-dollar bills each of them have.

26. The length and width of a rectangle in cm are two consecutive even integers. The length is $\frac{5}{4}$ of the width.
   (a) Find the sum of the length and width.
   (b) Find the perimeter of the rectangle.
   (c) If both the length and the width are increased by 6 cm,
      (i) find the increase in the perimeter of the rectangle,
      (ii) will $\frac{\text{new length}}{\text{new width}}$ be equal to $\frac{5}{4}$? Explain briefly.

27. (a) In a book, a chapter consists of 10 pages. The sum of the page numbers of the chapter is 1,025. Find the starting page number of this chapter.
   (b) If twice the total number of pages of the book is 26 more than three times the starting page number of this chapter, find the total number of pages in the book.

28. (a) The tens digit of a two-digit number is 5 more than the units digit. The number formed by reversing the digits is 128 less than twice the original number. Find the original number.
   (b) Let T be the sum of any two-digit number and the number formed by reversing its digits. Show that T is always a multiple of a certain number.

29.

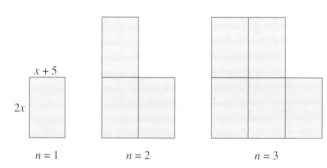

$n = 1$ $n = 2$ $n = 3$

The diagram shows some patterns formed by rectangular tiles of $2x$ cm by $(x + 5)$ cm.
   (a) Draw the pattern for $n = 4$.
   (b) Find the perimeter of the pattern for $n = 1, 2, 3$, and 4.
   (c) If the perimeter of the 4th pattern is 200 cm, find the value of x.
   (d) Find the value of n such that the perimeter of the pattern is 710 cm.

6 Ratio, Rate, And Speed

Basic Practice

1. Express each ratio in the simplest form.
   (a) $5 : 20$
   (b) $14 : 35$
   (c) $36 : 21$
   (d) $7.5 : 12.5$
   (e) $0.64 : \dfrac{2}{5}$
   (f) $\dfrac{8}{9} : \dfrac{16}{27}$
   (g) 40 cents : \$3
   (h) 320 cm : 2 m
   (i) 3 min : 80 s
   (j) 0.5 lb : 36 oz

2. Express each ratio in the simplest form.
   (a) $4 : 12 : 20$
   (b) $35 : 60 : 45$
   (c) $12 : 36 : 9$
   (d) $1.4 : 5.6 : 7$
   (e) $0.6 : 3.3 : \dfrac{3}{2}$
   (f) 5 in. : $\dfrac{5}{4}$ ft : $\dfrac{15}{2}$ ft
   (g) \$2.40 : 300 cents : \$4.50
   (h) 56 cm : 320 mm : 0.8 m
   (i) 20 min : 1 hr : 3,000 s
   (j) 0.6 kg : $\dfrac{3}{4}$ kg : 400 g

3. Find the ratio $x : y : z$ in the simplest form if
   (a) $x : y = 2 : 5$ and $y : z = 5 : 12$,
   (b) $x : y = 3 : 7$ and $y : z = 7 : 10$,
   (c) $x : y = 1 : 4$ and $y : z = 8 : 9$,
   (d) $x : y = 13 : 8$ and $y : z = 4 : 11$,
   (e) $x : y = 5 : 4$ and $y : z = 6 : 5$,
   (f) $x : y = 1 : 12$ and $y : z = 18 : 7$,
   (g) $x : z = 3.5 : 18$ and $y : z = 2 : 9$,
   (h) $x : y = \dfrac{2}{3} : 3$ and $x : z = 1 : 2$.

4. Find the value of x in each of the following.
   (a) $x : 3 = 4 : 9$
   (b) $x : 36 = 7 : 6$
   (c) $x : \dfrac{9}{5} = 25 : 3$
   (d) $2x : 5 = 14 : 25$
   (e) $4x : 7 = 8$
   (f) $8 : x = 2 : 5$
   (g) $12 : x = 4 : 3$
   (h) $7 : 2x = 14 : 1$
   (i) $5 : 3x = 7\dfrac{1}{2}$
   (j) $1\dfrac{1}{3} : x = \dfrac{1}{12}$

5. Kathy can key in 6 letters every 3 seconds using the message function in her mobile phone.
   (a) Find the number of letters Kathy can key in every second.
   (b) Hence, find the number of letters Kathy can key in
      (i)   in 9 seconds,
      (ii) in half a minute.
   (c) How many seconds would Kathy take to key in a 45-letter message?

6. Helena bought 16 pens for $7.20.
   (a) Find the cost of 1 pen.
   (b) Hence, find the cost of
      (i)   7 pens,
      (ii) a dozen pens.
   (c) Find the number of pens Helena can buy with $11.25.

7. The total mass of 14 balls is 2,100 g.
   (a) Find, in kg, the mass of 1 ball.
   (b) Hence, find, in kg, the mass of
      (i)   6 balls,
      (ii) 22 balls.
   (c) The total mass of x balls is 4,500 g. Find the value of x.

8. Convert the following speeds to km/hr and mph.
   (a) 6 m/s
   (b) 7.5 m/s
   (c) 11 m/s
   (d) 24 m/s
   (e) 100 m/s
   (f) 330 m/s

9. Convert the following speeds to m/s and mph.
   (a) 72 km/hr
   (b) 45 km/hr
   (c) 18 km/hr
   (d) 86.4 km/hr
   (e) 28 km/hr
   (f) 100 km/hr

10. John walks at an average speed of 0.6 m/s for 25 minutes.
   (a) Convert 0.6 m/s to km/hr.
   (b) Calculate the distance covered by John in km.

11. Find the ratio $p : q$ in the simplest form if

(a) $8p = 6q$,

(b) $3p = 7q$,

(c) $0.4p = 5q$,

(d) $2.4p = 1.8q$,

(e) $\frac{1}{5}p = \frac{1}{3}q$,

(f) $\frac{6}{7}p = \frac{3}{4}q$,

(g) $\frac{3q}{p} = 15$,

(h) $\frac{7q}{8p} = \frac{21}{56}$.

12. Find the ratio $m : n$ in the simplest form for each of the following.

(a) $4m + 4n = 3m + 9n$

(b) $9m - 3n = 5m - n$

(c) $2m - 7n = -4m + 8n$

(d) $10m - 8n = 16n - 6m$

13. (a) If $x : y = 3.5 : 4\frac{1}{2}$ and $y : z = \frac{3}{4} : 2.25$,

    (i) simplify $x : y$ and $y : z$,

    (ii) find $x : y : z$.

(b) If $6a = 5b$ and $8b = 3c$,

    (i) find $a : b$ and $b : c$,

    (ii) find $a : b : c$.

(c) If $15p + q = 10p + 11q$ and $20q - 23r = 12q - 7r$

    (i) find $p : q$ and $q : r$,

    (ii) find $p : q : r$.

14. The weekly allowance Rachel and Jane each receive are in the ratio $2 : 1$. If Rachel gives \$8 to Jane, the ratio becomes $2 : 3$. Let Jane's weekly allowance be \$$x$.

(a) Form an equation in terms of x and solve it.

(b) How much weekly allowance do Rachel and Jane each receive?

15. The sides of a right-angled triangle are in the ratio $5 : 12 : 13$. The difference in the lengths between the longest side and the shortest side is 28 cm. Calculate

(a) the longest side of the triangle,

(b) the perimeter of the triangle,

(c) the area of the triangle.

16. A private tutor charges \$120 for every 100 minutes of instruction given. If a student wants to extend the duration of the instruction to 2 hours, how much would the tutor charge according to the same rate?

17. The length of a side of a cubical container is 20 cm.

(a) Find the base area and volume of the container.

(b) Suppose that 100 cm^3 of water is poured into the container every 20 seconds. Find, in minutes and seconds, the time taken to fill the container

    (i) completely,

    (ii) to a depth of 12 cm.

(c) (i) Find the volume of water in the container after 8 minutes and 30 seconds.

    (ii) Hence, find the corresponding depth of the water.

18. The total cost of 5 identical textbooks is $43. If the 5 textbooks are stacked together, their combined thickness is 9.5 cm.

(a) Find the cost and the thickness of 1 textbook.

(b) The combined thickness of n textbooks is 24.7 cm. Calculate

   (i) the value of n,

   (ii) the total cost of these n textbooks.

(c) The total cost of m textbooks is $77.40. Calculate

   (i) the value of m,

   (ii) the combined thickness of these m textbooks.

19. A car travels at an average speed of 49.6 mph for half an hour on an expressway. It then travels at an average speed of 31 mph for 10 minutes on a road before arriving at its destination.

(a) Calculate the total distance traveled in miles.

(b) Calculate the total time taken in hours.

(c) Hence, calculate the average speed of the car for the whole journey.

20. Alex jogs for 15 minutes at an average speed of 4 mph. He then walks at an average speed of 2.4 mph for t minutes. The total distance traveled is 1.4 miles.

(a) Convert 15 minutes and t minutes to hours.

(b) Form an equation in terms of t and solve it.

(c) Hence, calculate Alex's average speed for the whole journey.

21. A tour bus departs from Town A at $08:50$ A.M. for Town B. From $08:50$ A.M. to $12:00$ P.M., the average speed of the bus is 75 km/hr. The driver then stops for an hour to allow all passengers to have lunch. At $1:00$ P.M., the tour bus sets off again and covers the remaining distance of 87.5 km at an average speed of 43.75 km/hr.

(a) (i) Calculate the time taken for the second part of the journey.

   (ii) Hence, find the arrival time of the tour bus in Town B.

(b) Calculate the total distance from Town A to Town B.

(c) Hence, calculate the average speed of the tour bus for the entire journey. Give your answer correct to the nearest km/hr.

Challenging Practice

22. (a) Initially, 3 solutions, A, B, and C, are mixed in the ratio $3 : 4 : 5$ by volume. The difference in the volumes between solutions A and C is 300 cm^3.

   (i) Calculate the volume of each solution in the mixture.

   (ii) Write down the volume of the mixture.

(b) The mixture is heated for 10 minutes. The volume of the mixture before and after heating is in the ratio $2 : 1$. The volume of solution C before and after heating is in the ratio $15 : 8$. Calculate the volume of

   (i) the mixture after heating,

   (ii) solution C after heating.

(c) The volumes of solutions A, B, and C are now in the ratio $3 : 2 : x$.

   (i) Form an equation in terms of x and solve it.

   (ii) Hence, calculate the volumes of solutions A and B after heating.

23. $600 is shared among 3 friends in the ratio $(2w + 3) : (w + 2) : (3w + 4)$, where w is a positive number.
   (a) If the smallest share is $125, form an equation in terms of w and solve it.
   (b) Hence, express the ratio in the simplest form.
   (c) The 3 friends decide to donate $50 each to a charity. Find the ratio of their shares after the donation.

24. A contractor, Mr. Parker charged his customer $100 for painting a rectangular ceiling of length 5.4 m and width 3 m. Another contractor, Mr. Lewis charged his customer $115 for painting a rectangular ceiling of length 5.7 m and width 3.2 m. Suppose that the quality of the workmanship of both contractors are the same and that both their charges are based on the area to be painted.
   (a) In terms of charges, which of the 2 contractors offers a better deal? Explain your answer.
   (b) Mr. Parker finished his paint job in 49 minutes. On average, how much time did he take to paint every m^2? Give your answer correct to the nearest minute.
   (c) How long did Mr. Lewis take to finish his paint job if he paints at the same rate as Mr. Parker? Give your answer correct to the nearest minute.

25. (a) At 07:00 A.M., Mr. Jackson drives from home to the stadium which is 6 km away. Find his average driving speed if he arrives at the stadium at 07:09 A.M.
   (b) After warming-up, Mr. Jackson jogs for $33\frac{1}{3}$ minutes at an average speed of 2 m/s on the 400-m running track. How many rounds does he complete on the running track?
   (c) Mr. Jackson leaves the stadium 1 hour after he arrives. If he must reach home by 08:15 A.M., calculate his average driving speed.
   (d) Hence, find the ratio of his average speed on the way to the stadium to his average speed on the way back home.

26. A and B are points along a jogging track which are 7.29 km apart. At 09:00 A.M., Yvonne starts to jog from A towards B at an average speed of 1.5 m/s. At 09:15 A.M., Hobert starts to jog from B towards A at an average speed of x m/s. Yvonne and Hobert meet at 09:45 A.M.
   (a) How far has Hobert jogged before he meets Yvonne?
   (b) (i) Form an equation in terms of x and solve it.
       (ii) Hence, find Hobert's average speed in km/hr.
   (c) Hobert rests for 10 minutes at the point where he meets Yvonne before jogging towards A at the same average speed.
       (i) At what time does Hobert reach point A?
       (ii) Calculate his average speed from B to A in m/s. Give your answer correct to 2 decimal places.

Enrichment

27. In the diagram, a beaker is full of water and oil. The ratio of the volume of water to the volume of oil is 2 : 1. If 50 cm^3 of oil is poured out, the ratio becomes 5 : 2.
   (a) Find the capacity of the beaker.
   (b) The density of water is 1 g/cm^3 and the density of oil is 0.8 g/cm^3. Find the average density of the liquid in the beaker. Give your answer correct to 3 decimal places.

28. Ken and Winston can polish pots at the rates of 3 pots per minute and 5 pots per minute respectively.

(a) The ratio of the hourly wage of Ken to that of Winston is the same as the ratio of the number of pots polished by them in an hour. If the hourly wage of Ken is $12, find the hourly wage of Winston.

(b) Ken began to polish a batch of 135 pots. Five minutes later, Winston joined him and they worked together.

    (i) How long would Winston take to finish the job?

    (ii) How many pots did Ken polish altogether?

29. The ratio of the balances in the savings accounts of Alex, Barry, and Charles is 9 : 5 : 4. If Alex transfers $180 to Charles, then the ratio becomes 27 : 20 : 25. Find the account balance of each person.

30. A truck and a car drive uniformly along an expressway from city A to city B. The truck leaves at 09 : 15 A.M. and arrives at 1 : 15 P.M. The car leaves at 10 : 00 A.M. and arrives at 12 : 45 P.M. At what time does the car overtake the truck?

7 Percentage

Basic Practice

1. Express the following fractions as percentages.

   (a) $\dfrac{3}{10}$

   (b) $\dfrac{39}{100}$

   (c) $\dfrac{2}{5}$

   (d) $\dfrac{4}{25}$

   (e) $\dfrac{9}{50}$

   (f) $1\dfrac{7}{20}$

   (g) $3\dfrac{13}{25}$

   (h) $5\dfrac{9}{10}$

2. Express the following decimals as percentages.

   (a) 0.23

   (b) 0.49

   (c) 0.51

   (d) 0.77

   (e) 2.56

   (f) 3.48

   (g) 10.24

   (h) 24.96

3. Express the following percentages as fractions.

   (a) $6\dfrac{3}{8}\%$

   (b) $15\dfrac{1}{3}\%$

   (c) $24\dfrac{2}{9}\%$

   (d) $80\dfrac{5}{12}\%$

   (e) $98\dfrac{7}{36}\%$

   (f) $156\dfrac{4}{11}\%$

   (g) $512\dfrac{4}{9}\%$

   (h) $1,475\dfrac{5}{7}\%$

4. Express the following percentages as decimals.

   (a) 12%

   (b) 56%

   (c) 73%

   (d) 92%

   (e) 146%

   (f) 278%

   (g) 553%

   (h) 1,249%

5. (a) Arrange 0.5, $\dfrac{2}{5}$, 45%, and 53% in ascending order.

   (b) Arrange 3.6, $3\dfrac{4}{5}$, 350%, and 375% in descending order.

6. Express the first quantity as a percentage of the second quantity.
  (a) 68 g of 2 kg
  (b) $0.45 of $2.50
  (c) 9 s of 2 min
  (d) 18 mm of 30 cm
  (e) 3.4 kg of 500 g
  (f) $1.20 of 75 cents
  (g) 1 hour of 12 min
  (h) 3.2 m of 64 cm

7. Find the value of the following.
  (a) 45% of $18
  (b) 31.25% of 224 cm
  (c) 12.75% of 48 kg
  (d) $22\frac{2}{9}$% of 90 min
  (e) $117\frac{3}{5}$% of $5,000
  (f) 115% of 80 cm
  (g) 215% of 400 g
  (h) 242.5% of 360 s

8. Find the unknown quantity in each of the following.
  (a) 12% of w kg is 36 kg.
  (b) $24\frac{2}{5}$% of x cm is 122 cm.
  (c) $91\frac{1}{4}$% of $$y$ is $36.50.
  (d) 3.125% of z minutes is 9 minutes.
  (e) 225% of a kg is 11.25 kg.
  (f) 145% of b m is 435 cm.
  (g) 350% of $$c$ is $19.25.
  (h) 240% of d minutes is 2 hours.

9. (a) The original price of a camera is $450. Find the new price if it is increased by 15%.
  (b) The original floor area of an apartment is 85 m². Find the new floor area if it is extended by 10% after upgrading.
  (c) At the beginning of a particular year, a factory had 600 workers. How many workers remained at the end of the year if 9% of them left during the year?
  (d) Before the air-conditioner is turned on, the temperature of a room is 34°C. Find the new temperature if it decreases by 35% after the air-conditioner is turned on.

10. (a) Compared to February, the number of chairs made in a factory in March is increased by 7.5% to 21,500. Find the number of chairs made in February.
  (b) The price of an electric fan increases by 25% to $48.75. Find the original price of the fan.
  (c) After attending a weight-loss program, Lydia's mass decreases by 12.5% to 63 kg. Find her original mass.
  (d) The duration of a television show decreases by 30% to 42 minutes if advertisements are excluded. Find the duration of the show if advertisements are included.

11. (a) Mr. Thomson bought a house in 2003 for $450,000. He sold it in 2006 for $567,000. Find the percentage increase in price.
  (b) Michelle's weekly allowance was $20 and $35 in the 6th grade and the 7th grade respectively. Find the percentage increase in her allowance.
  (c) The price of a sofa set before and after a sale was $2,450 and $2,009 respectively. Find the percentage decrease in price.
  (d) The average speed of a car on and off an expressway is 80 km/hr and 43.2 km/hr respectively. Find the percentage decrease in the average speed.

12. Suppose all items in a department store are sold at a discount of 12%. In the department store, the selling price of a shirt is $33 and the marked price of a pair of pants is $75. Find
   (a) the marked price of the shirt,
   (b) the selling price of the pair of pants,
   (c) the total amount of discount if a shirt and a pair of pants are bought.

13. The marked price, inclusive of a 7% sales tax of a dining table is $658.05.
   (a) Find
      (i) its price before the sales tax,
      (ii) the amount of sales tax paid.
   (b) Express the sales tax paid as a percentage of the marked price. Give your answer correct to 2 decimal places.

(**Further Practice**)────────────────────────────────

14. Mandy has a collection of 80 triangular stamps and 120 rectangular stamps. 35% of the triangular stamps and 18 of the rectangular stamps are fifty-cent stamps. Find
   (a) the percentage of triangular stamps,
   (b) the total number of fifty-cent stamps,
   (c) the percentage of fifty-cent stamps.

15. Two boys and one girl in a class of 40 answered 'Yes' when asked if the statement 'There are 100 minutes in an hour.' is true. Suppose that the ratio of the number of boys to the number of girls in the class is 3 : 2. Find
   (a) the number of boys and girls in the class,
   (b) the percentage of students who answered correctly,
   (c) the percentage of girls who answered wrongly,
   (d) the percentage of boys who answered wrongly.

16. Of the 1,200 participants who took part in a walkathon, 12% completed their walk in less than 35 minutes, 912 completed their walk in or after 35 minutes and the rest did not complete their walk. Find
   (a) the number of participants who completed their walk in less than 35 minutes,
   (b) the percentage of participants who completed their walk,
   (c) the percentage of participants who did not complete their walk.

17. Suppose that 82% of 7th grade students who took an English test passed and 45 students failed.
   (a) Find the number of students who passed.
   (b) The number of absent students was 2% of the number of students who took the test.
      (i) How many students were absent?
      (ii) Find the total number of 7th grade students in the school.

18. A charity concert starts at 8 P.M. The organizer estimated the concert is 40% through after 50 minutes.

    (a) **(i)** Find the estimated duration of the concert in hours and minutes.

        (ii) At what time is the concert estimated to end?

    (b) A sum of $28,800 is raised from the concert. Given that this amount of money is 10% short of the targeted amount, find how much the targeted amount is.

19. **(a)** In 2005, 45% of 1,020 workers in a factory were male. Find the number of male and female workers in 2005.

    (b) In 2006, 14 more female workers were employed to replace 9 male workers who resigned. Find, correct to 2 decimal places,

        (i) the percentage increase in the number of female workers,

        (ii) the percentage decrease in the number of male workers.

20. The length of a side of a cube is 10 cm.

    (a) Find the base area and volume of the cube.

    (b) Suppose both the length and width of the cube are increased by 10%. Find the new base area of the cube.

    (c) If the volume of the cube is unchanged after the increase in length and width of the cube in **(b)**, find, correct to 1 decimal place,

        (i) the new height of the cube,

        (ii) the percentage decrease in the height of the cube.

21. Anthony walks for 10 minutes and covers 0.6 km. He jogs for the next 40 minutes, increasing his average jogging speed by 80% over his average walking speed. He then runs for the last 10 minutes, increasing his average running speed by 150% over his average jogging speed.

    (a) Find, in km/hr, his

        (i) average walking speed,

        (ii) average jogging speed,

        (iii) average running speed.

    (b) Hence, find his average running speed as a percentage of his average walking speed.

    (c) Find his average speed for the whole journey.

22. **(a)** Jacqueline bought a refrigerator from a department store for $900. She then sold it to her sister at a 15% discount. How much did her sister pay for the refrigerator?

    (b) Jacqueline could have bought the refrigerator at a 10% discount if she had spent an additional x on any other items at the department store. Given that the overall percentage discount on all her purchases would then be 7.5%, find the value of x.

23. The marked price, inclusive of 7% sales tax, of a home theater system is $9,095 before the Christmas sale. During the Christmas sale, the home theater system is offered at a 5% discount. The first 50 customers are also entitled to an additional discount of 5% on the discounted price.

    (a) How much is the home theater system excluding sales tax before the Christmas sale?

    (b) Find the amount paid by the

        (i) 51st customer,

        (ii) 15th customer.

24. The following table shows Kenneth's results in 4 tests.

Test Number	Score	Maximum Possible Score
1	6.5	10
2	12	20
3	19	25
4	28	40

(a) In which test was Kenneth's performance the best? Explain your answer.

(b) For each test, grade 'A' is given if the score is more than or equal to 70% of the maximum possible score. Find, as a percentage, the number of times Kenneth was given grade 'A'.

(c) Suppose that 67.5% of the students in Kenneth's class were given grade 'A' at least once in the 4 tests. Find the number of students who were not given grade 'A' in any of the tests if there are 40 students in the class.

25. (a) A fruit crate contains a mix of 80 apples and oranges. If 21.25% of the fruits are rotten, find the number of rotten fruits.

(b) Suppose that 30% of the apples and $\frac{1}{5}$ of the oranges are rotten. Find the number of

    (i) rotten apples,

    (ii) rotten oranges.

(c) Hence, express the number of apples as a percentage of

    (i) the number of fruits,

    (ii) the number of oranges.

26. Eligible clients of a bank are offered 2 repayment schemes for a one-year loan.
    Scheme A: Pay $50 and 105% of the loan at the end of the one-year period
    Scheme B: Pay 103% of the sum of $200 and the loan at the end of the one-year period

(a) (i) Which is a better scheme for Mr. Martin to use if he is eligible for the loan and wants to borrow $10,000?

    (ii) How much will he save if he selects the better scheme?

(b) Mr. Carter, another eligible client, also borrowed from the bank. Find his loan amount if his payment by either of the schemes is the same.

27. (a) If X is 25% less than Y, by how many percent is Y more than X?

(b) If X is 25% more than Y, by how many percent is Y less than X?

(c) If X is decreased by 10% and then increased by 10%, find the percentage change in X.

(d) If Y is increased by 10% and then decreased by 10%, find the percentage change in Y.

28. Initially, a contractor quoted the labor cost and material cost, inclusive of sales tax, to renovate a house as $5,550 and $9,450 respectively. Suppose the sales tax rate is 7%.
  (a) Write down the total renovation cost.
  (b) Express the labor cost as a percentage of the total renovation cost.
  (c) Suppose that the material cost increases by 9%. The contractor offers to absorb 50% of the increase in the material cost by giving a discount of x% on the labor cost.
    (i) Find the value of x correct to 2 decimal places.
    (ii) Express the increase in renovation cost as a percentage of the initial renovation cost.
  (d) The new renovation cost is inclusive of sales tax. Find, correct to the nearest dollar, how much the contractor will charge if the sales tax is also waived.

> (Enrichment)

29. Funds were collected in a school to assist the family of a student. Aaron donated 20% of his pocket money. Barbara donated 25% of her pocket money. Carlo donated $33\frac{1}{3}$% of her pocket money. It is given that each of them donated the same amount of money.
  (a) Find the percentage of the total amount of pocket money of these 3 students that had been donated.
  (b) If the total amount of their donation was $72, find the amount of
    (i) Aaron's pocket money,
    (ii) Carlo's pocket money,
    (iii) Aaron's pocket money as a percentage of the amount of Carlo's pocket money.

30. A box contains 150 marbles, of which 60% are green and the remaining are red.
  (a) How many green marbles have to be removed from the box so that the percentage of green marbles becomes 52%?
  (b) If the number of green marbles is increased by 20% and the number of red marbles is decreased by 10%, find
    (i) the percentage change in the number of marbles in the box,
    (ii) the number of red marbles as a percentage of the number of green marbles.

31. In the 7th grade classes in a school, there are 24 more boys than girls. Let n be the number of 7th grade boys.
  (a) Express the percentage of boys in the 7th grade classes in terms of n.
  (b) If the percentage of boys in the 7th grade classes is 55%, find the total number of 7th grade students.

32. The marked price of a mobile phone was $840, including 5% sales tax. The sales tax was increased to 7%. Find
  (a) the percentage increase in the sales tax,
  (b) the percentage increase in the marked price of the mobile phone,
  (c) the percentage of discount on the new marked price so that the mobile phone was sold at the old price $840.
  Give your answers correct to 2 decimal places if necessary.

8 Angles, Triangles, And Quadrilaterals

1. In each case, find the angle that is complementary to the given angle.
   (a) 35°
   (b) 21°
   (c) 63°
   (d) 79°
   (e) 15.4°
   (f) 48.5°

2. In each case, find the angle that is supplementary to the given angle.
   (a) 74°
   (b) 123°
   (c) 86°
   (d) 142°
   (e) 155.6°
   (f) 94.5°

3. In each figure, *XOY* is a straight line. Find the measure of each unknown marked angle.

   (a)

   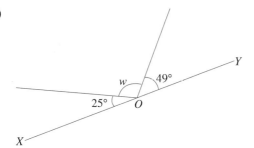

   (b)

   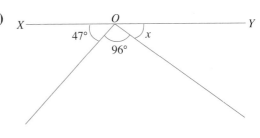

   (c)

   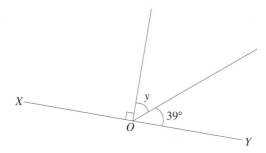

   (d)

   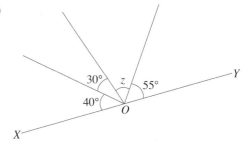

4. Find the measure of the unknown marked angle in each figure.

(a)

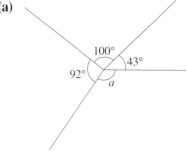

(b)

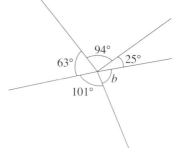

(c)

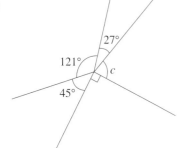

(d)

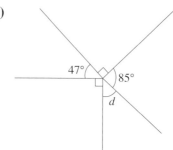

5. In each of the figures, the straight lines *AB* and *XY* intersect at point *O*. Find the measure of each of the following unknown marked angles.

(a)

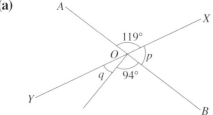

(b)

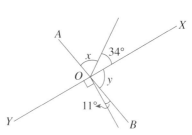

(c)

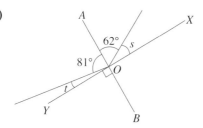

(d)

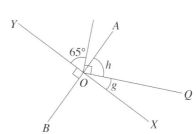

6. Draw each of the following line segments and construct a perpendicular bisector for each of them.
   (a) *PQ* = 12 cm
   (b) *ST* = 10 cm
   (c) *XY* = 9 cm

7. Draw each of the following angles and construct an angle bisector for each of them.
   (a) *m∠ABC* = 78°
   (b) *m∠FGH* = 132°
   (c) *m∠LMN* = 250°

8. (a) (i) Using a ruler and compasses only, draw a line segment *MN* 6 cm long and construct the perpendicular bisector of *MN*.

    (ii) Label the midpoint of *MN* as *O*.

  (b) Mark a point *V* which is on the perpendicular bisector and 4 cm above *O*.

  (c) Measure and write down the lengths of *MV* and *NV*.

9. (a) Construct △*XYZ* in which *XY* = 13 cm, *YZ* = 5 cm, and *XZ* = 12 cm.

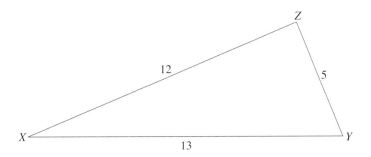

  (b) Measure all the angles of △*XYZ* and give your answers correct to the nearest degree.

  (c) Classify △*XYZ* by its angles.

  (d) Hence, estimate the area of △*XYZ*.

10. Find the values of *x* and *y* in each of the following diagrams.

  (a) *ABCD* is a rhombus.
                                         (b) *PQRS* is a rectangle.

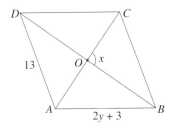
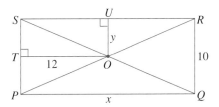

  (c) *HIJK* is a rhombus.

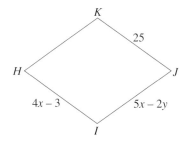

11. (a) Construct a rhombus $ABCD$ in which $AC = 8$ cm and $BD = 4$ cm.

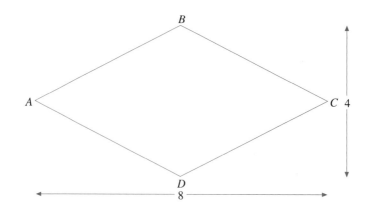

(b) Measure the length of AB and give your answer correct to the nearest 0.1 cm.

(c) (i) Measure $\angle BAD$ and give your answer correct to the nearest degree.

    (ii) Hence, find the measure of $\angle BCD$.

Further Practice

12. In each case, find the value of x if the given angles are complementary.

   (a) $30°$ and $3x°$ **(b)** $24°$ and $(20 + x)°$

   (c) $51°$ and $(70 - x)°$ **(d)** $8x°$ and $7x°$

   (e) $3x°$ and $1\frac{1}{2}x°$ **(f)** $(2x + 50)°$ and $(x + 4)°$

   (g) $(33 - x)°$ and $(3x + 5)°$

13. In each case, find the value of y if the given angles are supplementary.

   (a) $124°$ and $4y°$ **(b)** $77°$ and $(15 + y)°$

   (c) $134°$ and $(69 - y)°$ **(d)** $9y°$ and $11y°$

   (e) $\frac{3}{4}y°$ and $60°$ **(f)** $(5y + 26)°$ and $(4y + 64)°$

   (g) $(96 - 7y)°$ and $(10y + 15)°$

14. In each figure, ABC is a straight line. Find the value of x in each figure.

(a)

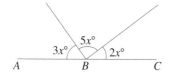

(b)

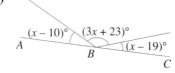

(c)

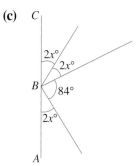

(d)

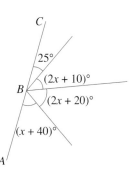

(e)

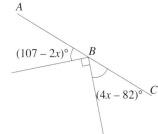

(f)

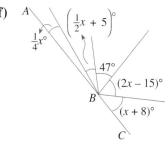

15. Find the value of x in each figure.

(a)

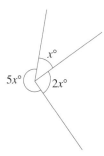

(b)

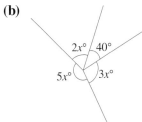

(c)

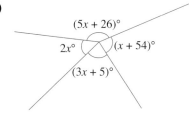

(d)

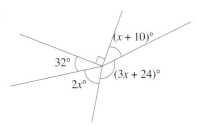

(e)

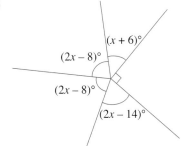

(f)

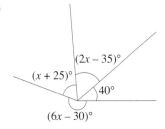

16. In each of the figures, the straight lines *AB*, *CD*, and *EF* intersect at point *O*. Find the value of *x* in each figure.

(a)

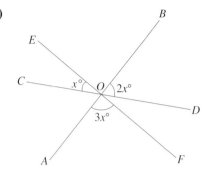

(b)

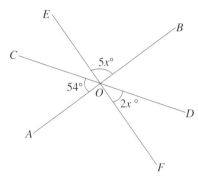

(c)

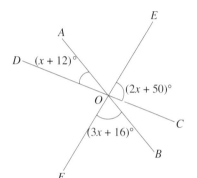

(d)

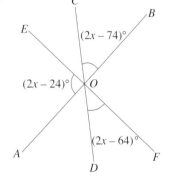

17. (a) Draw the given figure using a ruler and a protractor.

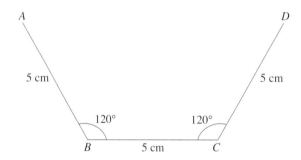

(b) Using a ruler and compasses only, construct the angle bisectors of ∠*ABC* and ∠*DCB*. Label the point where the two angle bisectors meet as *X*.

(c) (i) Measure ∠*BXC* and give your answer correct to the nearest degree.

(ii) Hence, write down a special angle property of △*BXC*.

18. (a) Using a ruler, a set square, and compasses only,

(i) draw a horizontal line segment *PQ* 12 cm long and construct the perpendicular bisector of *PQ*,

(ii) draw a vertical line segment *PR* 8 cm long and construct the perpendicular bisector of *PR*.

(b) (i) Label the midpoints of *PQ* and *PR* as *X* and *Y* respectively.

(ii) Label the point where the two perpendicular bisectors meet as *M*.

(c) (i) Name the figure which is enclosed by the line segments *MX*, *XP*, *PY*, and *YM*.

(ii) Hence, calculate the perimeter and area of the enclosed figure.

19. In the figure, *WXY* is a straight line and $m\angle YXZ = 132°$.

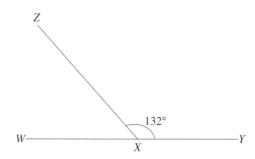

   (a) Draw the given figure using a ruler and a protractor.
   (b) Construct *XA* and *XB*, the angle bisectors of $\angle WXZ$ and $\angle YXZ$ respectively using a ruler and compasses.
   (c) **(i)** Find $m\angle AXW$ and $m\angle BXY$.
   (ii) Hence, show that $\angle AXW$ and $\angle BXY$ are complementary.

20. In the diagram, *WXYZ* is a square and *O* is the center of the square.

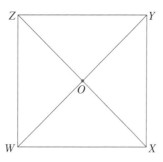

   If $OW = (2w + 7)$ cm and $OY = (3w - 5)$ cm, calculate
   (a) the value of *w*,
   (b) the length of *XZ*,
   (c) the area of *WXYZ*.

21. **(a)** Construct triangle *PQR* such that $PQ = 8$ cm, $QR = 6$ cm, and $m\angle PQR = 60°$.
   (b) Measure the length of *PR* and give your answer correct to the nearest 0.1 cm.
   (c) **(i)** Construct *PA*, the angle bisector of $\angle QPR$.
   (ii) Measure $\angle QPA$ and give your answer correct to the nearest degree.

22. **(a)** Using a ruler and compasses, construct $\triangle XYZ$ with $XY = 10$ cm, $YZ = 9$ cm, and $XZ = 6$ cm.
   (b) **(i)** Construct the angle bisector of $\angle XZY$.
   (ii) Construct the perpendicular bisector of *YZ*.
   (iii) Label the point where the angle bisector of $\angle XZY$ meets the perpendicular bisector of *YZ* as *P*.
   (c) **(i)** Construct a line which is parallel to *YZ* and passes through *P*.
   (ii) The parallel line in **(c)(i)** meets *XY* and *XZ* at *Q* and *R* respectively. Label the points *Q* and *R*.
   (iii) Measure the length of *QR*.

23. (a) (i) Draw a horizontal line *AB* 12 cm long.

   (ii) Construct above *AB*, the quadrilateral *ABCD* in which *AC* = 13 cm, *BC* = 5 cm, *AD* = 9 cm, and *BD* = 15 cm.

(b) Measure ∠*ABC* and ∠*BAD* and give your answers correct to the nearest degree.

(c) What type of quadrilateral is *ABCD*?

Challenging Practice

---

24. The figure shows the face of a round wall clock.

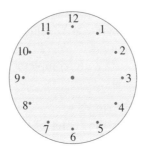

(a) Find the acute angle between the hour hand and the minute hand at 2 P.M.

(b) Find the obtuse angle between the hour hand and the minute hand at 7 A.M.

(c) Find the reflex angle between the hour hand and the minute hand at 10 P.M.

25. Three identical rectangular blocks are placed on a horizontal ground as shown. Each block touches an edge of the other two blocks. Find the value of *w*.

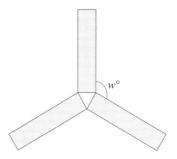

26. In the diagram, *ABCD* is a rhombus, *EAD* is a straight line, *AD* = *AE*, *AB* = 8 cm, and *m*∠*BCD* = 120°.

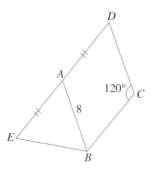

(a) Find *m*∠*BAE*.

(b) (i) Classify △*ABE* by its sides.

   (ii) Hence, find *m*∠*ABE*.

(c) Find the perimeter of the quadrilateral *BCDE*.

27. Figure I shows 3 lines, *AE*, *AC*, and *AF* which are drawn on both sides of a piece of square paper *ABCD* such that *m*∠*BAE* = *m*∠*EAC* = *m*∠*CAF* = *m*∠*FAD*. Four copies of *ABCD* are placed together as shown in Figure II.

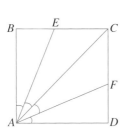

Figure I

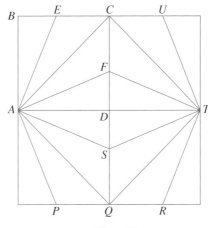

Figure II

(a) What types of quadrilaterals are *ASTF*, *AQTC*, and *ATUE*? Explain your answers.

(b) What type of triangle is △*EAP*? Explain your answer.

28. (a) (i) Draw a horizontal line *PQ* 14 cm long.

   (ii) Construct above *PQ*, a quadrilateral *PQRS* in which *m*∠*PQR* = 70°, *m*∠*QPS* = 50°, *m*∠*PQS* = 45°, and *QR* = 6 cm.

(b) Measure

   (i) the size of ∠*QRS* and give your answer correct to the nearest degree,

   (ii) the length of *QS* and give your answer correct to the nearest 0.1 cm.

(c) Construct the angle bisector of ∠*QRS*.

(d) The angle bisector of ∠*QRS* and the line segment *QS* meet at *X*.

   (i) Label the point *X*.

   (ii) Measure the length of *PX* and give your answer correct to the nearest 0.1 cm.

(**Enrichment**)

29.

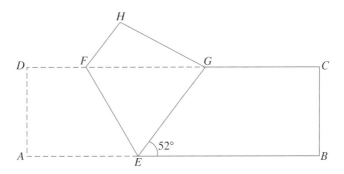

In the figure, *ABCD* is a rectangular strip of paper. The corner *A* is folded up to meet the edge *CD* at *G* and the crease *EF* is formed. It is given that *m*∠*BEG* = 52°.

(a) Find *m*∠*GEF*.

(b) What is the relationship between *DF* and *HF*?

(c) If the side *BC* is folded to coincide with the edge *CD*, find the angle between the crease and *CD*.

30. It is given that $m\angle A = (5x - 13)°$ and $m\angle B = (3x + 7)°$. Find the value of x if $\angle A$ and $\angle B$ are
  (a) complementary angles,
  (b) supplementary angles,
  (c) acute angles (Note: the solution is not unique).

31. (a) Draw the perpendicular bisectors of the sides of each of the following triangles using a straight edge and compasses only.

(i)

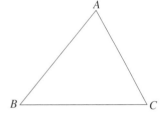

(ii)

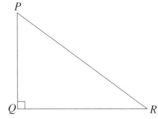

(iii)

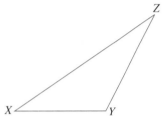

  (b) What do you observe from the constructions in **(a)**?

32. Using a ruler and compasses only, construct an angle of
  (a) 30°,   **(b)** 120°,
  (c) 22.5°,   **(d)** 75°.

Answers

Chapter 1   Factors And Multiples

Basic Practice

1. (a) 1, 2, 3, 6, 9, 18
   (b) 1, 2, 4, 5, 10, 20
   (c) 1, 2, 3, 4, 6, 8, 12, 24
   (d) 1, 2, 3, 5, 6, 10, 15, 30
   (e) 1, 3, 5, 9, 15, 45
   (f) 1, 2, 5, 10, 25, 50
   (g) 1, 3, 7, 9, 21, 63

2. (a) 4, 8, 12, 16, 20
   (b) 15, 30, 45, 60, 75
   (c) 17, 34, 51, 68, 85
   (d) 21, 42, 63, 84, 105
   (e) 35, 70, 105, 140, 175
   (f) 42, 84, 126, 168, 210
   (g) 100, 200, 300, 400, 500

3. (a) 2^5 (b) $2^2 \times 3^4$
   (c) $4^3 \times 7^4$ (d) $5^4 \times 8^3$
   (e) 11^3 (f) $3^2 \times 7^3$

4. (a) $2^5 \times 3$ (b) $2^3 \times 3 \times 5$
   (c) $2^4 \times 3^2$ (d) $2^3 \times 3 \times 5^2$
   (e) $3^3 \times 5^2$ (f) $2^3 \times 5^3$
   (g) $3^3 \times 7^2$

5. (a) 2^4 (b) $2^3 \times 3^3$
   (c) $2^2 \times 3^5$ (d) $2^3 \times 5^4$
   (e) $2^3 \times 3^2 \times 7^2$

6. (a) 9   (b) 6
   (c) 8   (d) 1
   (e) 21   (f) 14
   (g) 39   (h) 18
   (i) 49

7. (a) 20   (b) 18
   (c) 120   (d) 112
   (e) 90   (f) 72
   (g) 102   (h) 252
   (i) 1,050

8. (a) 8   (b) 12
   (c) 16   (d) 18
   (e) 20   (f) 24
   (g) 25

9. (a) 3   (b) 4
   (c) 5   (d) 10
   (e) 12   (f) 14
   (g) 16

10. (a) False, 9 is not a prime number.
    (b) False, 2 is a prime number.
    (c) True.
    (d) True.

Further Practice

11. (a) 5^7 (b) 7^6
    (c) 2^3 (d) 3^8
    (e) 3^{14} (f) 5^8
    (g) 7^{14}

12. (a) 6   (b) 7
    (c) 3   (d) 17
    (e) 23   (f) 15
    (g) 9   (h) 21

13. (a) 180   (b) 252
    (c) 2,346   (d) 336
    (e) 770   (f) 5,880
    (g) 9,240   (h) 88,200

14. (a) $3^3 \times 5^3$
    (b) (i) 15   (ii) 75
        (iii) 125   (iv) 1,125

15. (a) (i) 3^3 (ii) $3^2 \times 11$
        (iii) $3^3 \times 5$
    (b) (i) 3^2 (ii) $3^3 \times 5 \times 11$

16. (a) (i) $2^2 \times 3^4$ (ii) $2^4 \times 3^3$
    (b) (i) 3   (ii) 4

17. (a) (i) 93   (ii) 62
    (b) (i) 31   (ii) 186

18. (a) $2^3 \times 3^4$
  (b) (i) 2   (ii) 9

19. (a) $2^3 \times 3^2 \times 5^2 \times 7$
  (b) (i) $2^2 \times 3 \times 5 \times 7$
   (ii) $2 \times 3 \times 5 \times 7$
   (iii) $2 \times 3 \times 5$

20. (a) $2^6 \times 5^6$
  (b) (i) $2^3 \times 5^3$ (ii) $2^2 \times 5^2$

Challenging Practice

21. (a) (i) 15 cm   (ii) 3,375 cm^3
  (b) 36

22. (a) 160
  (b) 4 packs of cookies, 2 bottles of mineral water, and $5 cash.

23. (a) 180   (b) 20

24. (a) 120
  (b) (i) 2 hr   (ii) 4 : 30 P.M.

25. (a) (i) 14 cm   (ii) 56 cm
   (iii) 196 cm^2
  (b) (i) 8

Enrichment

26. (a) 2012, 2020, 2024 (Answers may be any valid leap years.)
  (b) The numbers of the leap years are multiples of 4.
  (c) Monday

27. (a) 41
  (b) 11, 9, and 5 or 15, 11, and 3
  (c) 5

28. (a) 2, 3, 5, 7, 11, 13, 17, 19
  (b) 28
  (c) 4

29. (a) 36 tiles, 252 cm
  (b) 7 cm
  (c) 480

Chapter 2 Real Numbers

Basic Practice

1. (a) <   (b) >
  (c) <   (d) <
  (e) >   (f) >
  (g) >   (h) <

2. $A = 1$, $B = 3$, $C = -2$, $D = 1.5$, $E = -2.5$, $F = 3.5$, $G = -0.75$, $H = 0.25$

3. (a) (i)

   $-2 < 3$

   (ii)

   $-3 < 1.5$

   (iii)

   $-4 < -\dfrac{1}{2}$

  (b) (i)

   $4\dfrac{1}{2} > -2$

   (ii)

   $1 > -0.5$

   (iii)

   $-1.5 > -3\dfrac{1}{2}$

4. (a) 7   (b) 0
  (c) 8   (d) -17
  (e) 66   (f) -50
  (g) 11   (h) 50

5. (a) (i) 5   (ii) 36
   (iii) 21   (iv) 18
  (b) 80

6. (a) -42 (b) -60
  (c) 40   (d) -8
  (e) -4 (f) 4
  (g) 25   (h) -125
  (i) -9 (j) -27

7. (a) $\dfrac{3}{7}$ (b) $\dfrac{2}{5}$
  (c) $\dfrac{7}{2}$ or $3\dfrac{1}{2}$ (d) $-\dfrac{3}{4}$
  (e) $-\dfrac{19}{6}$ or $-3\dfrac{1}{6}$ (f) $-\dfrac{25}{16}$ or $-1\dfrac{9}{16}$

8. (a) $1\dfrac{1}{8}$ (b) $1\dfrac{5}{24}$
  (c) $\dfrac{1}{9}$ (d) -27
  (e) 6   (f) $-\dfrac{3}{5}$
  (g) $-\dfrac{16}{21}$ (h) $1\dfrac{1}{8}$

9. (a) 0.375   (b) 2.65
    (c) −0.075   (d) −1.875
    (e) −3.06   (f) 0.36
    (g) 2.89   (h) −0.125

10. (a) $-1, -\dfrac{2}{3}, 0.088, 0.72, \dfrac{9}{2}$

    (b) $0.69, \dfrac{1}{5}, -\dfrac{3}{2}, -2.5, -5$

11. (a) $25\dfrac{3}{8}$ (b) $11\dfrac{13}{20}$
    (c) 8.717797887   (d) 4.641588834
    (e) −2.00904404   (f) −66
    (g) −0.125   (h) $29\dfrac{1}{4}$

12. (a) (i) 4,562   (ii) 643
      (iii) 0   (iv) 200
    (b) (i) 40   (ii) 790
      (iii) 8,930   (iv) 1,000
    (c) (i) 100   (ii) 200
      (iii) 4,300   (iv) 1,000

13. (a) (i) 5.4   (ii) 31.2
      (iii) 68.7   (iv) 10.0
    (b) (i) 3.14   (ii) 54.13
      (iii) 67.57   (iv) 10.00
    (c) (i) 2.718   (ii) 8.657
      (iii) 65.235   (iv) 5.000

14. (a) (i) 8,627 cm   (ii) 8,630 cm
      (iii) 86 m
    (b) (i) 59,485.7 g   (ii) 59,490 g
      (iii) 59,500 g   (iv) 59 kg
      (v) 60 kg

15. (a) 85, 86, 87, 88, 89, 90, 91, 92, 93, or 94
    (b) 89

16. (a) 2,849   (b) 2,750

Further Practice

17. (a) Shirley's score is increased by 4 points.
    (b) The price of every hamburger was increased by 50 cents.
    (c) The temperature of the conference room is decreased by 3°C.
    (d) Keanu walked 100 m northwards from his house to the bus stop.

18. (a) −15   (b) −48
    (c) $6\dfrac{7}{9}$ (d) $8\dfrac{3}{5}$
    (e) 36   (f) 8
    (g) 27

19. (a) $<$ (b) $=$
    (c) $>$ (d) $<$
    (e) $>$

20. (a) 17   (b) 10
    (c) 28   (d) 15
    (e) 11   (f) 0
    (g) 7

21. (a) $24 \div (2 \times 4) = 3$
    (b) $30 - (4 + 5) - 5 = 16$
    (c) $28 - 5 \times (2 + 1) = 13$
    (d) $-36 \div (3 + 6) + 4 = 0$
    (e) $6 + (36 \div 2) - 4 = 20$
    (f) $(3 \times 5 - 4) \times 2 = 22$

22. (a) $\dfrac{1}{9}$ (b) 4
    (c) 12   (d) 89
    (e) 0   (f) 0
    (g) 17   (h) 0

23. (a) $\dfrac{2}{135}$ (b) $\dfrac{49}{64}$
    (c) $-\dfrac{1}{6}$ (d) $\dfrac{1}{3}$
    (e) $-\dfrac{1}{48}$ (f) $\dfrac{7}{45}$
    (g) $-\dfrac{11}{45}$

24. (a) $\dfrac{3}{8}$ (b) $-\dfrac{2}{15}$
    (c) $\dfrac{4}{9}$ (d) 20

25. (a) $\dfrac{11}{15}, \dfrac{10}{13}, \dfrac{9}{11}$ (b) $\dfrac{13}{8}, \dfrac{11}{7}, \dfrac{17}{11}$

26. (a) 8   (b) 50,653
    (c) 300   (d) 10.25
    (e) 0.767614482   (f) 22.33662911
    (g) 521.2108639

27. (a) (i) $0.3\overline{4}$ (ii) $0.1\overline{5}$
      (iii) $1.5\overline{3}$ (iv) $2.\overline{5}$
    (b) 0.344, 0.156, 1.533, 2.556

28. (a) 3,108,319.54
    (b) (i) 3,108,319.5   (ii) 3,108,320
      (iii) 3,108,320   (iv) 3,000,000

29. (a) 0.027   (b) 0.538
    (c) 1.067   (d) 6.167
    (e) −1.694

30. (a) 458.762
    (b) (i) 45,900   (ii) 459

Challenging Practice

31. **(a)** Monday and Wednesday
  (b) $6.50
  (c) Overall change in weekly allowance = +1.5
    Hence, Lisa received more than the usual amount of weekly allowance.

32. **(a)** 16°C
  (b) 2.5 km

33. **(a)** $\frac{3}{14}$
  (b) Harris

34. **(a)** 12 km away in the east of the naval base.
  (b) 1 hr 24 min
  (c) 9.24 P.M.

35. **(a)** Mr. Lewis
  (b) $199,455,593

36. **(a)** $64
  (b) Yes, the estimated amount is more than the exact bill.

Enrichment

37. **(a)** **(i)** 7   **(ii)** 5
    (iii) 1   **(iv)** 6
  (b) **(i)** 1   **(ii)** −1
  (c) $|x + y| \neq |x| + |y|$

38. **(a)** $(0.6 + 0.6 - 0.6 - 0.6) \times 0.6 = 0$
  (b) $(0.6 + 0.6) \div 0.6 - 0.6 \div 0.6 = 1$
  (c) $(0.6 + 0.6) \div (0.6 - 0.6 + 0.6) = 2$
  (d) $0.6 + 0.6 + 0.6 + 0.6 + 0.6 = 3$
  (e) $(0.6 + 0.6 + 0.6 + 0.6) \div 0.6 = 4$

39. **(a)** 16,900
  (b) 63

40. **(a)** $\frac{1}{7} = 0.\overline{142857}$
    $\frac{2}{7} = 0.\overline{285714}$
    $\frac{3}{7} = 0.\overline{428571}$
    $\frac{4}{7} = 0.\overline{571428}$
    $\frac{5}{7} = 0.\overline{714285}$
    $\frac{6}{7} = 0.\overline{857142}$
  (d) $0.\overline{650793}$

41. **(a)** correct to the nearest 0.1 cm
  (b) Anthony. We should not round the numbers in the intermediate steps.

(c) 0.0096 cm
(d) We cannot measure the thickness of a sheet by an ordinary ruler. This is because the scale of a ruler is not precise enough to measure the thickness.

42. **(a)** 54 m²   **(b)** 2
  (c) 15 cm

Chapter 3 Introduction To Algebra

Basic Practice

1. **(a)** $4w^2$ **(b)** $12p^2$
  (c) $15q^3$ **(d)** $32r^3$
  (e) $3x^2$ **(f)** $12y^2$
  (g) 3   **(h)** 2

2. **(a)** $6xy$ **(b)** $\frac{6y}{x}$
  (c) $\frac{9xw}{y}$ **(d)** $\frac{12y^2}{x}$
  (e) $5pq - 6r$ **(f)** $3x + \frac{4y}{z}$
  (g) $9p^2 + 10qr$ **(h)** $25b^2 - 6cd$

3. **(a)** −13   **(b)** 46
  (c) 111   **(d)** 34
  (e) 0.6   **(f)** $\frac{12}{25}$ or 0.48
  (g) −4   **(h)** $-4\frac{1}{4}$ or −4.25

4. **(a)** 22   **(b)** −7.2 or $-7\frac{1}{5}$
  (c) 45   **(d)** 10
  (e) 38   **(f)** −4
  (g) −106   **(h)** 152

5. **(a)** 4   **(b)** 154
  (c) 245   **(d)** 64
  (e) 24   **(f)** 5

6. **(a)** $(4y + z) - 3x$ **(b)** $\frac{2s}{t} + 5r$
  (c) x^2y^3 **(d)** $\frac{f + \sqrt{g}}{h}$
  (e) $\frac{a^2}{c^2}$ **(f)** $p^2 + q^3 + mn$

7. **(a)** $(15x + 24y)$ **(b)** $228

8. **(a)** $(10l + 4b)$ cm   **(b)** $10bl$ cm²

9. **(a)** $(3x - 4)$ years old   **(b)** $(3x + 1)$ years old

10. **(a)** $2w$ kg   **(b)** $(2w - 1.5)$ kg

11. 13

12. (a) $27a^3 - 16b^2$

    (b) (i) $\dfrac{9}{16}$ (ii) $-31\dfrac{7}{8}$

13. (a) 775   (b) $40\dfrac{1}{6}$

14. (a) $-\dfrac{1}{20}$ or -0.05 (b) $19\dfrac{2}{5}$ or 19.4

15. (a) $\$(b + 900n)$ (b) $48,600

16. (a) $16,500

    (b) 800 represents the monthly pay, in dollars, of one odd job worker.

    4,500 is the monthly fixed cost, in dollars, of running the factory.

17. (a) $48xy$

    (b) (i) xy m^2 (ii) $0.75

18. (a) $(13x + 12y)$ cm

    (b) (i) $\left(\dfrac{13x + 12y}{25}\right)$ cm/s   (ii) 24.8 cm/s

19. (a) $(2m + 4n)$ legs   (b) $\$(mx + ny)$

    (c) $9,255

20. (a) $\dfrac{1}{8}(2m - 5)v^2$ units   (b) 1,417.5 units

Challenging Practice

21. (a) $\$\left(\dfrac{y}{xz}\right)$

    (b) (i) $\$\left[\dfrac{y(2z + w)}{xz}\right]$ (ii) $xz - 2z - w$

       (iii) $\dfrac{xz - 2z - w}{x}$

22. (a) 25 m   (b) 45 m

    (c) 20 m

23. (a) (i) $\$\left(\dfrac{d}{m}\right)$ (ii) $\$\left(\dfrac{e}{n}\right)$

       (iii) $\$\left(\dfrac{3d}{m} + \dfrac{5e}{n}\right)$

    (b) $\$\left[3\left(\dfrac{d}{m} + 0.1\right) + 5\left(\dfrac{e}{n} - 0.05\right)\right]$

24. (a) $\left(\dfrac{x - 2y}{n}\right)$ cm   (b) 3 cm

25. (a) (i) 120   (ii) 40,320

      (iii) 3,628,800   (iv) 9,900

    (b) $n! = n(n - 1)!$

Enrichment

26. (a) (i) $\dfrac{3}{4}$ (ii) $\dfrac{4}{5}$

    (b) $\dfrac{n}{n + 1}$

    (c) $\dfrac{100}{101}$

27. (a)

n	1	2	3	4	5	6
$n(n + 5)$	6	14	24	36	50	66
$(n - 3)(n + 2)$	-6	-4	0	6	14	24
$n(n + 5) - (n - 3)(n + 2)$	12	18	24	30	36	42

    (b) The number $n(n + 5) - (n - 3)(n + 2)$ is a multiple of 6. In fact, the number is equal to $6(n + 1)$.

28. (a)

n	1	2	3	4	5
$n^2 + n$	2	6	12	20	30
$\dfrac{n}{n^2 + 1}$	2	3	4	5	6

    (b) $n(n + 1)$

    (c) n by $(n + 1)$ tiles

    (d) 47

Chapter 4   Algebraic Manipulation

Basic Practice

1. (a) $12x$ (b) $-7y$

    (c) $-9y$ (d) $14w$

    (e) $-17m$ (f) $3ab$

    (g) $9xy$ (h) st

2. (a) $6d + 6$ (b) $5e - 3$

    (c) $f - 14$ (d) $-6g$

    (e) $9x - 14y$ (f) $-6k$

    (g) $24p$ (h) $9m$

3. (a) $10 + 2x$ (b) $-6x - 21$

    (c) $12f - 20g$ (d) $15x + 12y - 9z$

    (e) $-5f + 3g$ (f) $28p + 12pq$

    (g) $-3wx + 4wy$ (h) $10ab - 15ac + 5ad$

    (i) $6rs + 36rt$ (j) $12wx - 3wy$

4. (a) $31 + 18q$ (b) $3x - 38$

    (c) $14y$ (d) 21

    (e) $-1 + p$ (f) $11a$

    (g) $6p - 18q$ (h) $11r + 13s$

    (i) $-20 - x + y$ (j) $3m - 3n$

5. (a) 3 **(b)** −2
(c) 12 **(d)** −5
(e) −21 **(f)** −16
(g) 12 **(h)** 12

6. (a) (i) −1 **(ii)** −3
(iii) 1 **(iv)** 8
(v) −6 **(vi)** −20
(b) (i) −11 **(ii)** 2
(iii) 10

7. (a) $4(c + 2)$ **(b)** $2(5 − 3d)$
(c) $3(−2m + 3)$ **(d)** $−6(2 + 3n)$
(e) $7(4y + x)$ **(f)** $5(4p − q)$
(g) $3(−5m + 3n)$ **(h)** $−4(x + 3y)$
(i) $15a(2b + 3)$ **(j)** $9y(2 − 3x)$

8. (a) $(2x + y)(3w + 1)$
(b) $(4b − 3c)(a − 2d)$
(c) $(7m − 5n)(4p − 5q)$
(d) $(9a + 2b)(2c + 3d)$
(e) $(3 + 4t)(1 + 2s)$
(f) $(5a − 6b)(1 + 6c)$
(g) $(9a + 2b)(c + d)$
(h) $(7x + 8y)(3z − 2)$
(i) $(2j − 7k)(2h − 5g)$
(j) $(3c − d)(2a − 5b)$
(k) $(3m + 4n)(−5p + 3q)$

9. (a) $\dfrac{4x + 5}{2}$ **(b)** $\dfrac{7y + 2}{3}$
(c) $\dfrac{9w + 3}{5}$ **(d)** $\dfrac{2x − 1}{2}$
(e) $−z − 5$ **(f)** $\dfrac{y + 2x}{4}$
(g) $\dfrac{−q}{2}$ **(h)** $2a + 3b$

10. (a) $3n + 6$ **(b)** $6n$
(c) $9n − 18$ **(d)** $(6n + 2)$ cm

Further Practice

11. (a) (i) $14x + 5y$ **(ii)** $−6a − 4b$
(iii) $17p − 22q$ **(iv)** $8x + 12y$
(b) (i) $−s − 10t$ **(ii)** $12w + 4r$
(iii) $6x + 13y$
(c) $5m + 6n$

12. (a) $−10 + 11m − 4n$ **(b)** $−2 + 7a − b$
(c) $−14 + 3p − 10q$ **(d)** $−1 − 2x + 3y$
(e) $−13 − 11x + 44y$ **(f)** $80 − 27p + 14q$
(g) $−10 + 3a + 3b$ **(h)** $1 − 4s − 2t$

13. (a) $−8 − 16a$ **(b)** $55 − 9w$
(c) $16 − 17c$ **(d)** $−10 + 17s$
(e) $−39w$ **(f)** $x + y$
(g) $12p + 8q$ **(h)** $2n$

14. (a) (i) $−2a + 3$ **(ii)** −2
(b) (i) $17b − 20c$ **(ii)** −112
(c) (i) $−2xy$ **(ii)** 30
(d) (i) $\dfrac{6}{5}p − \dfrac{11}{20}q$ **(ii)** 23.5
(e) (i) $8z + 7$ **(ii)** 39

15. (a) $\dfrac{11x − 5}{12}$ **(b)** $\dfrac{5y + 9}{6}$
(c) $\dfrac{7}{10}$ **(d)** $\dfrac{−6 + 3w}{10}$
(e) $\dfrac{35 + 6p}{15}$ **(f)** $\dfrac{29 + 9q}{10}$
(g) $\dfrac{3 − 56p − 26q}{12}$ **(h)** $8m + 20n$

16. (a) $2(3a + 2b − 6)$
(b) $2(4 − 3s − 6t)$
(c) $3(3a − 6b − 5c)$
(d) $16p(1 + 2q)$
(e) $3x(5y − 7 − 9z)$
(f) $2w(3x − 4y + 4z)$
(g) $2s(10p − 12q + 15r)$
(h) $−4(2f + 2g + 3h)$

17. (a) $(1 − a)(5 − b)$
(b) $(q − 2)(2r − 7)$
(c) $(3a − c)(2 − 5b)$
(d) $(c − 2d)(a − b)$
(e) $(7a + 2b)(3x − 4y)$
(f) $(4q + 5p)(5m − 3n)$
(g) $(3x + 2y)(3w − z)$

18. (a) (i) $8(p − 3pq + 2)$
(ii) 112
(b) (i) $(1 − 4h)(3f − 4g)$
(ii) 70
(c) (i) $(3x − 4y)(3w + 1)$ **(ii)** 40
(d) (i) $(a − 2b)(1 + 6c)$ **(ii)** 91

19. (a) 3,400 **(b)** 243
(c) 590 **(d)** −9,900
(e) 7,800 **(f)** 45.8
(g) −9,400 **(h)** 26,700

20. (b) (i) $(x + y)(2t + 1)$
(iii) $(4s + 3)(2t − 1)$

Challenging Practice

21. (a) (i) $(2n − 3)$ years **(ii)** $(9n − 8)$ years
(iii) $(12n − 11)$ years
(b) (i) 97 years **(ii)** 113 years

22. (a) (i) $4x + 8y$ **(ii)** $2x + 4y$
(b) $12x + 24y$
(c) 48

23. (a) (i) $\$\left(2x + 5y - 1\dfrac{1}{2}\right)$

    (ii) $\$\left(3x + 5y - 2\dfrac{1}{2}\right)$

  (b) Pack A

24. (a) (i) $(6xy + 3x)$ cm^2
    (ii) $(7xy + x)$ cm^2
  (b) $(xy - 2x)$ cm^2
  (c) (i) $x(y - 2)$

25. (a) $(2x - 5)(y + 3)$ (b) Marcus

Enrichment

26. (a) $T = \dfrac{40x}{3}$ (b) 6

27. (a) $4(2x + 3)$ cm
  (b) $(2x + 3)$ cm
  (c) (i) 68 cm
    (ii) 289 cm^2

28. (a)

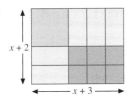

    $(x + 3)$ by $(x + 2)$ units
  (b) $(x + 3)(x + 2)$
  (c) $(x + 5)(x + 3)$

29. (a) $V = (3a + 2b)(4x - 5y)$
  (b) V is doubled.

Chapter 5   Simple Linear Equations In One Variable

Basic Practice

1. (a) 5   (b) 20
  (c) 3   (d) 5
  (e) -9 (f) 28
  (g) -45 (h) -18
  (i) 80   (j) 14

2. (a) -5 (b) $\dfrac{1}{2}$
  (c) -15 (d) 5
  (e) $10\dfrac{1}{2}$ (f) 5
  (g) -1 (h) 3
  (i) 3   (j) -1

3. (a) 8   (b) 10
  (c) -33 (d) 14
  (e) 5.5   (f) $\dfrac{1}{3}$
  (g) -1

4. (a) 7   (b) 5
  (c) -2 (d) 6
  (e) 13   (f) -1
  (g) 3   (h) $-\dfrac{1}{2}$

5. (a) 1.25   (b) -3
  (c) $-\dfrac{1}{2}$ (d) $-\dfrac{1}{2}$
  (e) 3   (f) -3
  (g) 9   (h) $\dfrac{1}{3}$

6. (a) $7\dfrac{1}{2}$ (b) -7
  (c) -1 (d) 5
  (e) -3 (f) 2
  (g) $6\dfrac{1}{8}$

7. (a) $8n + 5$
  (b) 15
  (c) (i) 125   (ii) 140

8. (a) 77, 78, 79   (b) 62, 64, 66
  (c) 35, 37, 39

9. (a) $(x - 12)$ cm   (b) 168 cm

10. (a) $3m$ years   (b) 13
  (c) 39 years

Further Practice

11. (a) $-1\dfrac{1}{4}$ (b) $3\dfrac{1}{2}$
  (c) $-2\dfrac{1}{2}$ (d) 8
  (e) $3\dfrac{1}{2}$ (f) $28\dfrac{3}{4}$
  (g) -21

12. (a) -60 (b) $\dfrac{1}{2}$
  (c) 8   (d) 3
  (e) 2   (f) $\dfrac{2}{3}$
  (g) -3.5 (h) $\dfrac{3}{4}$

13. (a) 5   (b) -2
  (c) -5 (d) -42
  (e) 8   (f) -5.5
  (g) -3.25

14. (a) −7 (b) −19

(c) 1 (d) $−3\frac{1}{2}$

(e) $−1\frac{1}{2}$ (f) 2

(g) $1\frac{1}{2}$ (h) −3

15. (a) 5 (b) −2

(c) 21 (d) $\frac{3}{4}$

(e) 6 (f) $−2\frac{3}{4}$

(g) $2\frac{1}{2}$

16. (a) 7

(b) (i) 14 cm

(ii) $1\frac{1}{2}$

17. (a) 9

(b) 13 years

18. (a) 0.2

(b) (i) $0.80 (ii) $9.80

19. $\frac{5}{7}$

20. −12

Challenging Practice

21. (a) (i) $\frac{1}{5}$ (ii) $\frac{1}{6}$

(iii) $\frac{1}{x}$

(b) (i) $\frac{30}{11}$ (ii) 2 hr 44 min

22. (a) 08 : 30 A.M.

(b) 9 km

23. (a) 19 goats and 85 chickens

(b) each chicken: $8, each goat: $85

(c) $2,295

24. (a) (i) $P = 450 + 700N$

(ii) $3,950

(iii) 3

(b) (i) $P = 270 + 790N$

(ii) 2

25. (a) 15

(b) Raymond: $110

Wilson: $240

(c) Raymond: 1 ten-dollar bill and 2 fifty-dollar bills

Wilson: 14 ten-dollar bills and 2 fifty-dollar bills

Enrichment

26. (a) 18 cm

(b) 36 cm

(c) (i) 24 cm

27. (a) 98 (b) 160

28. (a) 83

29. (a)

$n = 4$

(b) For $n = 1$, $(6x + 10)$ cm

For $n = 2$, $(12x + 20)$ cm

For $n = 3$, $(14x + 30)$ cm

For $n = 4$, $(16x + 40)$ cm

(c) 10

(d) 21

Chapter 6   Ratio, Rate, And Speed

Basic Practice

1. (a) 1 : 4 (b) 2 : 5

(c) 12 : 7 (d) 3 : 5

(e) 8 : 5 (f) 3 : 2

(g) 2 : 15 (h) 8 : 5

(i) 9 : 4 (j) 2 : 9

2. (a) 1 : 3 : 5 (b) 7 : 12 : 9

(c) 4 : 12 : 3 (d) 1 : 4 : 5

(e) 2 : 11 : 5 (f) 1 : 3 : 18

(g) 8 : 10 : 15 (h) 7 : 4 : 10

(i) 2 : 6 : 5 (j) 12 : 15 : 8

3. (a) 2 : 5 : 12 (b) 3 : 7 : 10

(c) 2 : 8 : 9 (d) 13 : 8 : 22

(e) 15 : 12 : 10 (f) 3 : 36 : 14

(g) 7 : 8 : 36 (h) 2 : 9 : 4

4. (a) $1\frac{1}{3}$ (b) 42

(c) 15 (d) $1\frac{2}{5}$

(e) 14 (f) 20

(g) 9 (h) $\frac{1}{4}$

(i) $\frac{2}{9}$ (j) 16

5. (a) 2

(b) (i) 18 (ii) 60

(c) 22.5

6. (a) $0.45
  (b) (i) $3.15 (ii) $5.40
  (c) 25

7. (a) 0.15 kg
  (b) (i) 0.9 kg (ii) 3.3 kg
  (c) 30

8. (a) 21.6 km/hr, 13.392 mph
  (b) 27 km/hr, 16.74 mph
  (c) 39.6 km/hr, 24.552 mph
  (d) 86.4 km/hr, 53.568 mph
  (e) 360 km/hr, 223.2 mph
  (f) 1,188 km/hr, 736.56 mph

9. (a) 20 m/s, 44.64 mph
  (b) 12.5 m/s, 27.9 mph
  (c) 5 m/s, 11.16 mph
  (d) 24 m/s, 53.568 mph
  (e) $7\frac{7}{9}$ m/s, 17.36 mph
  (f) $27\frac{7}{9}$ m/s, 62 mph

10. (a) 2.16 km/hr (b) 0.9 km

Further Practice

11. (a) 3 : 4 (b) 7 : 3
  (c) 25 : 2 (d) 3 : 4
  (e) 5 : 3 (f) 7 : 8
  (g) 1 : 5 (h) 7 : 3

12. (a) 5 : 1 (b) 1 : 2
  (c) 5 : 2 (d) 3 : 2

13. (a) (i) $x : y = 7 : 9, y : z = 1 : 3$
    (ii) 7 : 9 : 27
  (b) (i) $a : b = 5 : 6, b : c = 3 : 8$
    (ii) 5 : 6 : 16
  (c) (i) $p : q = 2 : 1, q : r = 2 : 1$
    (ii) 4 : 2 : 1

14. (a) $x = 10$
  (b) Jane: $10, Rachel: $20

15. (a) 45.5 cm (b) 105 cm
  (c) 367.5 cm^2

16. $144

17. (a) 400 cm^2, 8,000 cm^3
  (b) (i) 26 min 40 s (ii) 16 min
  (c) (i) 2,550 cm^3 (ii) $6\frac{3}{8}$ cm

18. (a) Cost = $8.60, Thickness = 1.9 cm
  (b) (i) 13 (ii) $111.80
  (c) (i) 9 (ii) 17.1 cm

19. (a) $29\frac{29}{30}$ mi (b) $\frac{2}{3}$ hr
  (c) 44.95 mph

20. (a) 15 min = $\frac{1}{4}$ hr, t min = $\frac{t}{60}$ hr
  (b) $t = 10$
  (c) 3.36 mph

21. (a) (i) 2 hr (ii) 3:00 P.M.
  (b) 325 km
  (c) 53 km/hr

Challenging Practice

22. (a) (i) Volume of solution A = 450 cm^3
      Volume of solution B = 600 cm^3
      Volume of solution C = 750 cm^3
    (ii) 1,800 cm^3
  (b) (i) 900 cm^3
    (ii) 400 cm^3
  (c) (i) $x = 4$
    (ii) Volume of solution A = 300 cm^3
      Volume of solution B = 200 cm^3

23. (a) $w = \frac{1}{2}$
  (b) 8 : 5 : 11
  (c) 2 : 1 : 3

24. (a) Mr. Parker offers a better deal. His charges per m^2 is lower.
  (b) 3 min
  (c) 55 min

25. (a) 40 km/hr (b) 10
  (c) 60 km/hr (d) 2 : 3

26. (a) 3.24 km
  (b) (i) $x = 1.8$ (ii) 6.48 km/hr
  (c) (i) 10:33 A.M. (ii) 1.57 m/s

Enrichment

27. (a) 750 cm^3 (b) 0.933 g/cm^3

28. (a) $20
  (b) (i) 15 min (ii) 60

29. Alex: $720, Barry: $400, Charles: $320

30. 11:39 A.M.

Chapter 7　Percentage

Basic Practice

1. (a) 30%　　　　　　(b) 39%
   (c) 40%　　　　　　(d) 16%
   (e) 18%　　　　　　(f) 135%
   (g) 352%　　　　　(h) 590%

2. (a) 23%　　　　　　(b) 49%
   (c) 51%　　　　　　(d) 77%
   (e) 256%　　　　　(f) 348%
   (g) 1,024%　　　　(h) 2,496%

3. (a) $\frac{51}{800}$　　　　　(b) $\frac{23}{150}$
   (c) $\frac{109}{450}$　　　　(d) $\frac{193}{240}$
   (e) $\frac{707}{720}$　　　　(f) $\frac{86}{55}$
   (g) $\frac{1,153}{225}$　　　(h) $\frac{1,033}{70}$

4. (a) 0.12　　　　　　(b) 0.56
   (c) 0.73　　　　　　(d) 0.92
   (e) 1.46　　　　　　(f) 2.78
   (g) 5.53　　　　　　(h) 12.49

5. (a) $\frac{2}{5}$, 45%, 0.5, 53%
   (b) $3\frac{4}{5}$, 375%, 3.6, 350%

6. (a) 3.4%　　　　　　(b) 18%
   (c) 7.5%　　　　　　(d) 6%
   (e) 680%　　　　　(f) 160%
   (g) 500%　　　　　(h) 500%

7. (a) $8.10　　　　　(b) 70 cm
   (c) 6.12 kg　　　　(d) 20 min
   (e) $5,880　　　　(f) 92 cm
   (g) 860 g　　　　　(h) 873 s

8. (a) $w = 300$　　　(b) $x = 500$
   (c) $y = 40$　　　　(d) $z = 288$
   (e) $a = 5$　　　　(f) $b = 3$
   (g) $c = 5.5$　　　(h) $d = 50$

9. (a) $517.50　　　　(b) 93.5 m^2
   (c) 546　　　　　　(d) 22.1°C

10. (a) 20,000　　　　(b) $39
    (c) 72 kg　　　　　(d) 60 min

11. (a) 26%　　　　　(b) 75%
    (c) 18%　　　　　(d) 46%

12. (a) $37.50　　　　(b) $66
    (c) $13.50

13. (a) (i) $615　　　(ii) $43.05
    (b) 6.54%

Further Practice

14. (a) 40%　　　　　(b) 46
    (c) 23%

15. (a) Number of boys = 24; Number of girls = 16
    (b) 92.5%
    (c) 6.25%
    (d) $8\frac{1}{3}$ %

16. (a) 144　　　　　(b) 88%
    (c) 12%

17. (a) 205
    (b) (i) 5　　　　(ii) 255

18. (a) (i) 2 hr 5 min　(ii) 10.05 P.M.
    (b) $32,000

19. (a) 459 male workers, 561 female workers
    (b) (i) 2.50%
        (ii) 1.96%

20. (a) Base area = 100 cm^2; Volume = 1,000 cm^3
    (b) 121 cm^2
    (c) (i) 8.3 cm
        (ii) 17.4%

21. (a) (i) 3.6 km/hr　(ii) 6.48 km/hr
        (iii) 9.72 km/hr
    (b) 270%
    (c) 6.54 km/hr

22. (a) $765　　　　　(b) 300

23. (a) $8,500
    (b) (i) $8,640.25　(ii) $8,208.24

Challenging Practice

24. (a) Test 3　　　　(b) 50%
    (c) 13

25. (a) 17
    (b) (i) 3　　　　(ii) 14
    (c) (i) 12.5%　　(ii) 14.3%

26. (a) (i) Scheme B　(ii) $44
    (b) $7,800

27. (a) $33\frac{1}{3}$ %   **(b)** 20%
   (c) 1%   **(d)** 1%

28. (a) $15,000
   (b) 37%
   (c) (i) 7.66
       (ii) 2.835%
   (d) $14,416

Enrichment

29. (a) 25%
   (b) (i) $120
       (ii) $72
       (iii) $166\frac{2}{3}$ %

30. (a) 25
   (b) (i) 8%
       (ii) 50%

31. (a) $\dfrac{100n}{2n-24}$ %   **(b)** 240

32. (a) 40%   **(b)** 1.90%
   (c) 1.87%

Chapter 8   Angles, Triangles, And Quadrilaterals

Basic Practice

1. (a) 55°   **(b)** 69°
   (c) 27°   **(d)** 11°
   (e) 74.6°   **(f)** 41.5°

2. (a) 106°   **(b)** 57°
   (c) 94°   **(d)** 38°
   (e) 24.4°   **(f)** 85.5°

3. (a) 106°   **(b)** 37°
   (c) 51°   **(d)** 55°

4. (a) 125°   **(b)** 77°
   (c) 77°   **(d)** 48°

5. (a) $m\angle p = 61°$, $m\angle q = 25°$
   (b) $m\angle x = 67°$, $m\angle y = 79°$
   (c) $m\angle s = 28°$, $m\angle t = 9°$
   (d) $m\angle g = 25°$, $m\angle h = 65°$

8. (c) $MV = 5$ cm, $NV = 5$ cm

9. (b) $m\angle X = 23°$, $m\angle Y = 67°$, $m\angle Z = 90°$
   (c) $\triangle XYZ$ is a right triangle.
   (d) 30 cm²

10. (a) $m\angle x = 90°$, $y = 5$
   (b) $x = 24$, $y = 5$
   (c) $x = 7$, $y = 5$

11. (b) 4.5 cm
   (c) (i) 53°   **(ii)** 53°

Further Practice

12. (a) 20   **(b)** 46
   (c) 31   **(d)** 6
   (e) 20   **(f)** 12
   (g) 26

13. (a) 14   **(b)** 88
   (c) 23   **(d)** 9
   (e) 160   **(f)** 10
   (g) 23

14. (a) 18   **(b)** 37.2
   (c) 16   **(d)** 17
   (e) 32.5   **(f)** 36

15. (a) 45   **(b)** 32
   (c) 25   **(d)** 34
   (e) 42   **(f)** 40

16. (a) 30   **(b)** 18
   (c) 17   **(d)** 57

17. (c) (i) 60°
      (ii) $\triangle BXC$ is an equilateral triangle.

18. (c) (i) Rectangle
      (ii) Perimeter = 20 cm
         Area = 24 cm²

19. (c) (i) $m\angle AXW = 24°$, $m\angle BXY = 66°$

20. (a) 12
   (b) 62 cm
   (c) 1,922 cm²

21. (b) 7.2 cm
   (c) (ii) 23°

22. (c) (iii) $QR = 3$ cm

23. (b) $m\angle ABC = m\angle BAD = 90°$
   (c) Trapezoid

Challenging Practice

24. (a) 60°

(b) 150°

(c) 300°

25. 120

26. (a) 60°

(b) (i) Equilateral triangle

(ii) 60°

(c) 40 cm

27. (a) *ASTF* is a rhombus.

AQTC is a square.

ATUE is a trapezoid.

(b) △*EAP* is an isosceles triangle because *AE* = *AP*.

28. (b) (i) 130°

(ii) 10.8 cm

(d) (ii) 10.9 cm

Enrichment

29. (a) 64°

(b) *DF* = *HF*

(c) 45°

30. (a) 12

(b) 23.25

(c) One of the solutions is $x = 20$.

The **Dimensions Math Workbooks** are written as supplements to the textbooks in the Dimensions Math series for middle school students. They are designed to give the students more practice in applying the concepts learned.

The questions in each workbook chapter are categorized into 4 parts according to the level of difficulty and the thinking skills involved.

These comprehensive workbooks aim to give students the tools and the confidence to handle mathematical questions and apply mathematical concepts to real-life situations. By achieving this, students will find that learning mathematics is an interesting and exciting experience.

ISBN 978-981-4431-74-3

9 789814 431743